What p

PLAY

"This book humanises science, by exploring how things work in relation to how *we* work. And the key to this exploration is music. The brain as jazz band is a delightful analogy — a collection of cells that plays and improvises in harmony. No longer will it be thought of as a lump in the head on a trajectory of decay, but rather, an infinitely adaptable and playful part of all we are and know."

— STEPHEN HOUGH,
classical pianist, composer & writer

"What companies need today are adaptable, innovative and collaborative people. *Play Your Brain* convincingly demonstrates how to achieve this and strengthen your results by adopting a musical mindset. A must-buy for anyone working in ever-changing environments, and aiming to deliver out-of-the-box performance."

— ALEX MYERS,
President & CEO, ArjoHuntleigh

"A pioneer work in the emerging field of applied neuroscience, *Play Your Brain* likens the brain to a jazz band — in its capacity to improvise and make new connections. The authors show how to maximise its enormous potential, through immensely thoughtful, practical and brain-based suggestions. Highly recommended!"

— PAUL T. BROWN,
Visiting Professor in Organisational Neuroscience,
London South Bank University

"A masterpiece, and tight to the core, *Play Your Brain* is essential reading for all leaders and managers who want to orchestrate their employees and organisations to become highly self-regulated. Combining brain science with real-life examples, this book paves the way to implementation in relation to everyday challenges. One of those books you must have!"

— TOBIAS KIEFER,
Head of Global Learning & Development,
Booz & Company

"How do you acquire the readiness to change that is so sought after in today's business environment — but also so hard to achieve without the nearly insurmountable effort and cost of 'change programmes' and course activity? *Play Your Brain* shows you how. If playing certain 'keys' does not deliver — change! If you feel stuck on a key — change! If your 'melody' goes out of tune — change! Thus readiness to change and a flexible mindset become a natural part of your approach to life and business. An engaging and very approachable book for any layer of an organisation."

— HENRIETTE KISTRUP,
Supply Chain Director, Carlsberg UK

"Mathematics and melancholy, poetry and logic, narrow rules and grandiose dreams — all possible strategies and inspirations unite themselves in the musician. *Play Your Brain* makes clear how *everyone* can gain from approaching life and goals in musical ways. The inspirational potential of this book is immense."

— MORTEN ZEUTHEN,
Professor, Royal Danish Academy of Music

"*Play Your Brain* is like a wise friend offering tools and pointers for acting in useful ways and staying on top of situations. It is great to be able to 'look up inside yourself' when you need help. It creates energy to give — and this surely is what society needs today."

— LISBET THYGE FRANDSEN,
Group Senior Vice President, Grundfos Management

"How to adopt a musical mindset and create the change you want? Anette Prehn and Kjeld Fredens propose playing the eight keys of your 'inner piano,' to create a flexible state that adjusts to every situation — an invaluable ability in today's changeable world. *Play Your Brain* will help readers succeed in both life and career."

— YI-YUAN TANG, *Professor of Neuroinformatics,*
Dalian University of Technology

"*Play Your Brain* offers refreshing, new insight into how we can all grow and adapt, breaking the habits that hold us back. The idea of unlocking the magic of the musical mindset is a powerful one that will boost life and career coping around the globe."

— PAUL SATTI, *Managing Director,*
Novozymes Malaysia

"A brain expert and a coach. Neuroscience and sociology. Innovation and leadership development. Two very strong authors and an immensely important challenge: How may I understand myself better and become more skilled in reaching my goals? Anette Prehn and Kjeld Fredens have come together and written a very inspiring and useful book that introduces how to play eight 'keys' that will turn your brain into a co-player."

— STEEN HILDEBRANDT,
Professor of Management Studies, Aarhus University

PLAY YOUR BRAIN

ANETTE PREHN & KJELD FREDENS

PLAY
YOUR
BRAIN

Adopt a Musical Mindset and
Change Your Life & Career

Marshall Cavendish
Business

PO Box 65829
London EC1P 1NY
United Kingdom
info@marshallcavendish.co.uk

and

1 New Industrial Road
Singapore 536196
genrefsales@sg.marshallcavendish.com
www.marshallcavendish.com/genref

Marshall Cavendish is a trademark of Times Publishing Limited

Other Marshall Cavendish offices:
Marshall Cavendish International (Asia) Private Limited, 1 New Industrial Road, Singapore
536196 • Marshall Cavendish Corporation, 99 White Plains Road, Tarrytown NY 10591–
9001, USA • Marshall Cavendish International (Thailand) Co Ltd, 253 Asoke, 12th Floor,
Sukhumvit 21 Road, Klongtoey Nua, Wattana, Bangkok 10110, Thailand • Marshall Cavendish
(Malaysia) Sdn Bhd, Times Subang, Lot 46, Subang Hi-Tech Industrial Park, Batu Tiga, 40000
Shah Alam, Selangor Darul Ehsan, Malaysia

A CIP record for this book is available from the British Library

ISBN 978-981-4328-58-6

Cover design by OpalWorks
Printed and bound in the United Kingdom by TJ International Ltd

**Marshall Cavendish publishes an exciting range of books
on business, management and self-development.**

If you would like to:
- Find out more about our titles
- Take advantage of our special offers
- Sign up to our e-newsletter

Please visit our
special website at: www.business-bookshop.co.uk

Contents

Values

Appreciating the core of interplay

35

Body

Mastering your physical instrument

54

Perception

Directing your interpretations

74

Vision

Rehearsing the future

97

Goals

Making your dreams attainable

120

Emotions

Picking your emotional strings

139

Successes

Tapping into your achievements

161

All together now!

Playing the keys, creating the change

180

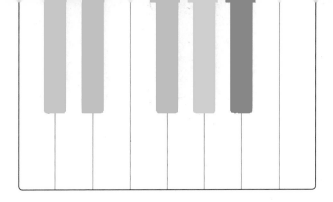

Introduction

Setting the tone

IT'S DEAD EASY to turn your brain into an opponent. The brain follows a certain logic and if you don't know what that is and how to make the most of it, you will continue to be the prisoner of a thousand ingrained habits. You may even be making life more difficult for yourself, because you are a novice in "playing your brain."

We have written this book to help you turn your brain into a co-player. It is an extraordinarily exciting world that will open up in the pages to come, and yet it can all be distilled to this simple formula:

Brain knowledge + Musical mindset ⇨ Successful change

1

You will get to know the core functions of the brain and thus expand your mental and behavioural repertoire substantially. But knowing the "what" is not enough. You need to find out "how" to play your brain so that you can switch fluently from one part of your repertoire to another.

No matter what field of achievement you look at, what characterises the best of the best is not merely impeccable knowledge of the rules of the game, but ease of execution, fluency, and improvisation — a sense of musicality.

It's possible to obtain brain knowledge in a dry, dispassionate way, as if you were merely studying a subject at school. But if you want it to work for you — and really pave the way to change — you must make a particular effort to work it "into the muscles."

You are likely to have embarked on journeys of change before in your life. The times when you were successful hold precious information about which strategies work well for you. However, your less-successful attempts are also important, and they may well have failed because you were working uphill, not knowing and not respecting brain logic.

Daily life entails going in and out of different roles, dealing with expectations, creating certain results. Playing your brain enables you to adjust and master the different situations and demands life is full of. You will literally change your brain connections and activity levels as well as your mental habits and behaviours. Metaphorically speaking, you will learn to tramp new neural paths in your brain, and return to these paths even when you feel you have walked astray.

The music in your brain

You may have heard people comparing the brain to a machine or a computer. A far more precise and eloquent metaphor is

actually a jazz band, because the brain works in truly musical ways. The 100 billion nerve cells it contains — also called neurons — spontaneously connect to one another. The many parts of the brain work together constantly, and the interplay, the network, is highly interesting. When certain areas are in play, they suppress other areas.[1] When certain connections are frequently used, they

Billions of nerve cells coordinate their activity in meaningful, harmonious ways.

become stronger. Those connections that are rarely or never used wither away. This is the brain's "use it or lose it" principle[2]: you either play with the band or you are out.

Modern brain researchers are no longer looking for the brain's "conductor," in the sense of a leader at the top of a hierarchy. Instead, they are researching the *principles* that make it possible for the brain's many billions of nerve cells to coordinate their activity in meaningful and harmonious ways.

This is where the jazz band comes in. If you listen to one, you will notice the "art of the ensemble" — a unique *total* result, achieved by a collection of players, with the resources available to them at that moment. None of the members is above or below the others; all of them coordinate their functions and make the most of their interplay. The result is an integrated, smooth-flowing piece of music, far greater than the sum of its parts.

Brain functions consist of constant fluctuations in tension states, which create patterns over time. In both music and human interaction, timing is of the essence: Which nerve cells fire when? Which ones fire at the same time? And how do you train these firings, so that the end result is coordinated and useful?

The model we introduce in this book uses just such a musical approach to master your mind and body. The model consists of

eight keys — like an octave on a piano — but you need not have any experience with music to start playing your "inner piano."

The eight keys of your inner piano

The brain knowledge you will gain is captured in these eight keys of your "inner piano" — Thoughts, Values, Body, Perception, Vision, Goals, Emotions, and Successes:

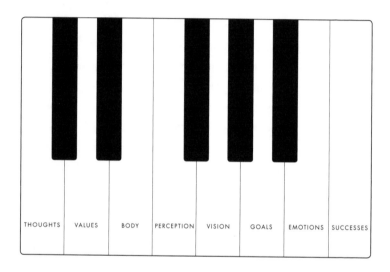

| THOUGHTS | VALUES | BODY | PERCEPTION | VISION | GOALS | EMOTIONS | SUCCESSES |

The keys represent the core brain functions you need to know in order to play your brain. Their order does not imply that you must always play them like that. You don't do that on a piano either. You can start off reading whichever chapter you find most interesting — and proceed to whichever one appeals to you next. Bearing in mind what the musician knows — that you only understand the beginning when you know the ending — you may in fact want to read the last chapter first. There we present a framework for playing the keys synchronically, which may be useful to know from the beginning.

In other words, feel free to make this book your own. Read it from A to Z if that's what works for you. When you choose to read it your own way, you become a *co-creator* of the book, and are well on your way to a musical mindset — adept at improvising, attuned to your curiosity, and alive to the numerous options ever present.

"Action" and "reflection" are integrated parts of this model. When you play the keys, you are in the process of performing an action; when you view your performance, you are reflecting at the same time. Action and reflection are not the same, but you must make them become

The musical mindset is a highly flexible one that adjusts to the needs of the situation.

two sides of the same coin. Some people act so much and so quickly that they never reach a state of reflection. Others reflect and reflect but never get out of the starting gates. The art of playing the brain lies in striking a balance between action and reflection, between that which creates results and that which creates perspective. The more masterful your play becomes, the closer action and reflection come to be merged. This is how it is for the best musicians — they reflect *while* they play — and this is also how it will be for you as you develop your play on your inner piano.

Naturally, you will play your brain with more fluency and greater awareness after half a year's practice, or two years of practice, but the good news is that your efforts will be meaningful and effective from the start. Through your training and experiences, you will become better and better at combining the keys, expanding your repertoire, and cultivating a multi-faceted playing style.

You may already know and use some of the keys of your inner

piano. But if you are like most people, you are probably playing the same keys again and again, or playing with only one finger or two instead of with all of them.

Adopting a musical mindset

Life contains tension and relaxation, heaviness and lightness, quick and slow tempos, the simple and the complex, light and dark, love and sorrow. If we translate these familiar experiences into sounds and tones, life could be described as a piece of music. Biologically speaking, music is in fact our first vocal language, communicating feelings and creating social relations; later comes verbal language, with its sharp, analytical qualities. Young children from all cultures and corners of the world prefer that you sing to them instead of talk.[3]

Musicians can do magic. They are musical at heart. And they have the ability to capture our souls and imaginations, and to immerse themselves into the activity they are in the midst of, to the extent where they form a unique unity with their instrument.

Musicians have learned to swing between experience and analysis, between seeing the big picture and focusing on the details. The musical brain is both holistic and analytic, both concrete and abstract. It uses both brain hemispheres far more frequently than the average person.[4]

The musical mindset of a musician is a highly flexible one that adjusts to the needs of the situation. Spontaneity goes hand in hand with the ability to follow through with a particular structure. What other people may consider opposites, say, structure and spontaneity, the musician considers inextricable parts of the same whole.

Music and musicians have the unique ability to hold contrasts in a meaningful way and to tell many different stories at the same

time. Thus, music shows us the way in today's complex world: it contains the key to understanding the interplay between complexity and simplicity, between the individual and its ever-shifting environment.

This interaction we have with our environment is a constant one, but it is not necessarily a smooth one. We often find ourselves feeling misunderstood, restricted, disrespected, excluded, trapped. It does indeed take an extensive repertoire, great knowledge of the "outer game" and the "inner game," and the ability to improvise as you go along to be a successful human being. Musicians know that timing is everything. So it is for the rest of us, in our daily encounters and interactions. A remark can win over an audience or leave them baffled — depending whether it comes at the "right" moment.

We all face cultural expectations, no matter which country, industry, organisation, network or family we are part of. But within these social boundaries, *you* are the one deciding what to play, when to play, and how to play. You are the one who can start paying attention to your own daily play, and improve its quality step by step.

Musicality is thus not just for musicians. It is for you; us; all human beings. Musicality is much more than the ability to play a particular instrument with flair and passion. Musicality means openness to what is present and what is desired, the ability to make the most of what is currently here. Musicality is found in world-class performances of any kind; it is found in the way some people interact with one another (interpersonal skills), and in the way some people interact with themselves (intrapersonal skills).

Musicality means openness to what is present and what is desired.

7

There are ten core assets of the musical mindset — inspired by that of the musician — that you should know when you embark on the journey of creating the change you want in your life and career. To make the translation to your inner piano easier, let's imagine a pianist with two "handfuls" of assets you may want to integrate into your own playing style.

The musician is:

① *Skilled* — has gotten to know each individual key through curiosity and practice, and has built a broad repertoire;

② *Synergistic* — knows the importance of making the keys sound together;

③ *Structured yet spontaneous* — is capable of following a score as well as improvising creatively;

④ *Flexible* — adapts to the demands of the situation and surroundings, and does so with a good sense of timing;

⑤ *Resilient* — has the power to quickly bounce back onto track when a mistake is made;

⑥ *Oscillating between experience and analysis* — uses the appropriate brain system (fast vs. slow);

⑦ *Collaborative* — has the socio-emotional skills to play together with others to create a multi-layered whole;

⑧ *Present* — can absorb himself or herself into the activity at hand, creating "flow" and top performances;

⑨ *Playful* — approaches life with optimism, humour, joy, and a spirit of experimentation;

⑩ *Patient* — knows that mastery does not come overnight, that all beginnings are difficult, and that results will come in time.

With these ten core assets in mind, take a look at yourself.

What does, say, "flexible" mean in your life? When are you most flexible? What enables and enhances this flexibility? What restricts it? How do you tune in to being flexible, even when you don't feel so? The better you become at bridging the insights of this book and your own life, the more you will gain out of it. It takes reflection and experimentation as you go along.

The plasticity of your brain

But what makes it possible, in the first place, to play your brain? It comes down to the *plasticity* of the brain — its ability to change.

Until the early 1990s, most brain researchers thought that we receive all our nerve cells at birth. They believed that the nerve cells died slowly after the age of 25, and that the connections in our brain gradually decreased in strength and complexity.

Today, advanced technology has given us new insights. We know that there are about 100 billion nerve cells that connect to one another through so-called synapses[5]; that at least 200 new nerve cells are created in the memory region alone each day, all through life.[6] In other words, the brain is in a state of constant change.[7]

The brain is in a state of constant change.

Likewise, until just a few years ago, researchers thought that there were specific centres in the brain for language, feeling, sight, balance, etc. Today, brain researchers conclude that it is a case of both and neither.[8] Basic functions, which deal with our motor activities and sensory feedback, are localised in particular brain regions, but compound cognitive functions are distributed, involving larger areas of the brain. All the eight keys in this book are distributed; none of them resides wholly in one particular region of the brain.

Functions like language, for example, are the result of

teamwork between many different areas of the brain — areas that can work together in widely different ways. This is why the construct of language varies from person to person, and why the structure of language changes all the time depending on the environment.

The brain is furthermore constantly reorganising itself. Researchers have found that functions lost can be rehabilitated with the help of *other* areas of the brain. The psychiatrist Norman Doidge considers it "one of the most extraordinary discoveries of the 20th century" that training, learning, and action can "turn our genes on or off, thus shaping our brain anatomy and our behaviour."[9] The neurologist Vilayanur Subramanian Ramachandran calls the discoveries within brain research in recent years the "Fifth Revolution."[10]

Training, learning and action can turn our genes on or off.

But even today, science has barely just begun to uncover the brain's myriad wonders. Through reading this book, you will come to understand a fragment — albeit a very important fragment — of all this.

In this book, when we speak of the brain, we refer to both the biological and mental brain, but mostly to the latter. The biological part deals with the brain's chemistry and physics, with neurotransmitters such as dopamine and serotonin, and with nerve-cell plasticity. The mental part deals with our ability to think and to act, and with our cognition in the broad sense of the word.

"But I already know a lot about the brain — what more do I need to know?" you might ask. If this is the case, you will be surprised, since many long-received notions of the brain are now obsolete. Some scientists once thought that the further down one

probed into the brain, the further back one would go in terms of human evolution, and that the civilised cortex enclosed the more basic and primitive functions.[11] If you have heard this popular story, you need to begin revising your image of the brain. The brain is neither composed of evolutionary layers, nor is it particularly modular. It functions much more like a network, and is far more complex and fascinating than we can grasp or imagine.

Others might say, "We are as we are — all this talk about change is just hot air." But they overlook the brain's essential plasticity, meaning that it is malleable and constantly changing and adapting to its environment. The nerve cells that you use to perform an action today are not precisely the same ones you will use when you perform the same action two weeks from now. In fact, your brain will not even look the same after you finish reading this book.

You develop your brain constantly, through the choices you make, and through what you "train" in your everyday life. The cabbies driving London's black taxis are an example of this brain plasticity. For two to four years, the drivers train to know all the roads, routes, and attractions within a 10-kilometre radius of the centre. Studies show that their brains develop a larger right hippocampus — and thus better spatial memory — than others. And the longer the cabbies train, the larger this part of the brain becomes.[12] What do *you* train in your daily life? Which parts of your brain are more well-trained than others?

Stimulated neurons develop 25 per cent more connections.

Some might believe that change is not for them: "I'm too old — you can't teach an old dog new tricks." But it has been shown that stimulated neurons develop 25 per cent more connections, and increase in size and blood supply. And this can happen

whether early or late in life.[13] The fact is that you can change, no matter your age. It does not necessarily happen in a jiffy, even though it may actually happen in a jiffy. A new realisation, a bit of fine-tuning — and what seemed insurmountable, overwhelming, and unrealistic suddenly takes on a different form, and you find yourself in the process of doing something quite different from what you were used to a short while ago.

The history of personal change is full of examples of both kinds of change: solid results built up over the course of dedicated training, as well as leaps of insight that change, in an instant, the way you look at yourself, at the world, and at all the possibilities around you.

Making the most of the time with yourself

Getting to know your brain and adopting a musical mindset is an investment, not least because you are together with yourself all the time. (For some people this is a terrifying prospect, because they lead themselves with a stick, or their inner dialogue is full of acrimony, so that their own company is not the most empowering one.)

Let us imagine that, in parallel with learning from this book, you also have a coach. Perhaps you have a one-hour coaching session every fortnight — a realistic set-up. This means that for each hour-long coaching session, you have 335 hours without the coach by your side, during which time your development hinges on your ability to self-coach.

This dependency on our inner play is not new; it has been a fundamental human circumstance all through history. And yet, learning to cope with those many hours is not something most people have learnt. Perhaps they lived in societies that did not wish to further such abilities; or the society's modes of production

made it unrealistic to spend time on it; or they did not have access to such knowledge — at least not to the extent now possible.

Today, more and more people find that society — and the workplace, in particular — expects them to master self-leadership and self-management. You must be able to plan, carry out, and develop your work, while being in tune with the company's goals and values. You must be able to motivate yourself and work independently, while delivering results every day. The demands are ever-growing, but yet, again, only very few of us have actually learned *how* to be self-dependent. We are just expected to know.

By learning to play the inner piano of your brain, you will get better at aligning yourself flexibly to such needs of the surroundings — and influencing them when relevant — while staying true to yourself. And as you play your brain, you will become more aware that you do it together with other "musicians" in the "ensembles" that you are part of. Try to make the most of your coordinated effort. Explore, too, **Explore adding value to something bigger than yourself and meaningful to many.** the satisfaction of playing together for a higher cause, adding value to something that is bigger than you and meaningful to many.

To be able to coach and lead yourself towards good results is thus not the same as being able to do it constructively, effectively, and with a smile on your lips. Our wish is that by playing your brain, your self-leadership will not only lead to results and effectiveness, but also to greater curiosity and happiness.

We hope that you are sitting comfortably — and that you are smiling. Did you know that when you smile before learning something new, you perform better?[14]

On the other hand, please do not sit too comfortably. Because

this book is not a cookbook, or a manual; it is not written for people who think they can just lean back and read it passively from start to end. There are no quick fixes here. You cannot stick out your arm, get a magic shot, and live happily ever after. This book invites you to become a co-creator, constantly making sense of what is written here in relation to your own reality and experiences.

This book invites you to become a co-creator.

You will have to think, and you will have to learn how to learn. You must awaken your inner philosopher, because, if we merely instructed you, you would never become self-sufficient. All research shows that you learn best when you are actively bridging what you are learning and your personal experience, when you internalise the learning and make it a part of you.

So, enjoy the exploration, experimentation, and investment. Let the music begin!

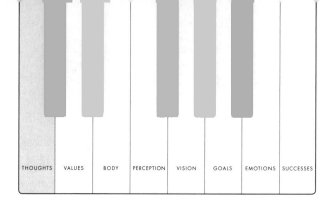

| THOUGHTS | VALUES | BODY | PERCEPTION | VISION | GOALS | EMOTIONS | SUCCESSES |

1

Thoughts

Tuning your mind for success

OUR THOUGHTS ARE powerful melodies that can make us feel better or worse. Any performer knows that a slight change of one's inner talk can completely tip a performance. In fact, outstanding performances are accompanied by a special inner silence: a mindful awareness and pure presence. Musicians know this as "becoming one with my instrument." This chapter explores how you tune your mind in similar ways, upgrading the quality of the thoughts you have, and creating the most useful melodies in your head.

The first step in creating change is retraining your thought patterns. This principle may sound simple, but it has far-reaching implications.

Thoughts are often formulated as questions: "What do I do

now?" "What does he think?" "Why does this keep happening?" And thought processes are often closely related to the contents of our inner dialogue.

Since the birth of civilisation, thoughts and questions have been crucial to the development of human potential. In classical Greek philosophy, Socrates turned asking questions into an art, and compared it to the work of a midwife: assisting in the delivery of insights and solutions.

What questions do we ask ourselves? Of what quality are they? And how do they prime our emotions and actions?

From judging to mindfulness

In the 1970s, a U.S. tennis coach named Timothy Gallwey had an epiphany that forever changed modern coaching philosophy. It had to do with the way human thoughts influence results.

One day, when Gallwey was not feeling particularly motivated, he took a more laid-back and passive approach than usual to his tennis students. To his surprise, he discovered that the students actually performed better now that he had stopped pointing out their mistakes and correcting their play. He also noticed that when a player tried to incorporate a correction into his game, his performance level dropped.

Gallwey realised that focusing on mistakes led his charges' attention to the mistakes and made them commit *more*. He saw, too, that you can "try too hard." The quality of the players' inner dialogue and thoughts became a focal point for him from then on.

Until that day, Gallwey's main contribution as a coach had been spotting errors and delivering instructions: "Turn your elbow more!" "Stop hitting so hard!" And so on. Now he discovered something far more effective. When the players adopted an attentive and curious approach to their own game, they corrected their own swings and performed better — by themselves. They became "self-regulating." Gallwey could not believe his eyes, but he explored the phenomenon further.

In 1975, he wrote a book, *The Inner Game of Tennis*, which begins with these words: "Every game is composed of two parts, an outer game and an inner game."[1] The outer game is the game we play in the outer world, whether it be a tennis match, a job interview, a work assignment, or a household chore; it is that which is visible to others. The inner game is the dialogue that takes place in our minds and thoughts.

Your inner game offers nourishment for your outer game, the performance.

If you do not master your inner game, Gallwey concluded, you are certain to lose the outer game. If your inner game is characterised by self-condemnation and commands, for example, it will invariably lead to lapses in concentration, nervousness, and anger. "It's gone wrong again." "Why do I always get so nervous? I just need to pull myself together." "Come on — do it now!" "I'm no good at public speaking." "I'm no good at maths." "It didn't work this time either." "Idiot!" These are all examples of self-condemnation and commands, which conflict with our ability to perform well. You probably have your own examples of how you issue orders to yourself.

After that epiphany, Gallwey instead invited his players to become aware of what it was they were doing, and what specifically was taking place. For instance, they learnt to take note of things like, "When my wrist is in this position, the ball flies 5 cm over the net," rather than saying, "That was a bad/good shot." The first is an example of a neutral, calm, observation-based, non-judgmental *description*; the second is an example of an *assessment*. It is essential to understand the difference, not just

in tennis, but also in social interaction, self-coaching, feedback, and life in general.

When you are present in this way, you sharpen your sensing of what is happening — not your assessment. Gallwey basically taught the players what researchers call "receptive attention." This is the part of the attention directed towards connections; it is process-oriented, and idea-generating. Receptive attention is opposed to "focused attention," which is result-oriented, directed towards components and details with the aim of assessing and controlling.

This inner tuning to receptive attention is also called "mindfulness." The amazing thing is that mindfulness has concrete effects inside of you: the alarm bell in your brain — the so-called amygdala — quietens; your cortisol (stress hormone) level goes down; your inner calm grows, and your immune system improves.[2] This is a great example of the interplay between the Thoughts key and the Body key on your inner piano (⇨BODY).

Mindfulness is more than simply relaxation. A study by Professor Yi-Yuan Tang compared the effects of a type of mindfulness training called "body-mind training" with the effects of "relaxation." The mindfulness group had almost 50 per cent greater immune function on average, and lower cortisol levels, than the relaxation group. These differences could be noted after just five days of training for twenty minutes a day.[3]

In other words, becoming mindful is a huge investment for both mental and physical health, and it boosts your openness to information from the external world too, as we shall see now.

Narrative circuitry vs. direct experience

To further understand how to access this neutral, calm, observation-based and non-judgmental presence, we must appreciate how we tune ourselves to our environment and experiences.

Researchers talk of "narrative circuitry" and "direct experience" as two opposing modes of experience.[4] They are inversely correlated — when one goes up, the other one goes down.

The narrative circuitry consists of the creation, repetition and recreation of a narrative via language and imagination — the stories we tell ourselves, the interpretations we make, the associations we get. This circuitry involves a network of brain regions such as the medial prefrontal cortex, and memory regions such as the hippocampus. You use this circuitry for planning, analysing, daydreaming, and ruminating; you take in information and add your interpretations. But, equally, you could also say that you activate your interpretations and thus filter what information you take in, in the first place.

The narrative circuit is dominant by default when the individual is not focused on the outside world but on his inner thoughts, and the brain is at wakeful rest. This state of mind creates new ideas and is an example of how the brain's *slow system* comes into contact with the *fast system* (⇨ VISION).[5]

Many people live most of their lives in this narrative circuitry.

What this means though, researchers point out, is that direct experience is to a large extent excluded. Direct experience — when the insula, the region of the brain that relates to perceiving bodily sensations,

The direct experience lets you see more options, which helps you make better choices.

and the anterior gyrus cinguli, the region central to switching your attention, become active — means being mindful. It means being in the now, sensing and perceiving much more data than when you are in the narrative circuit. The direct experience is important because "noticing more information lets you see more

options, which helps you make better choices, which makes you more effective at work."[6]

Each time you play the Thoughts key, make yourself aware whether you need lots of thoughts, verbalisations and inner dialogue right now — or whether you may actually gain from a more spacious awareness of what is going on. If your goal is to get to creative solutions verbal analysis can actually hinder and disrupt the pursuit.[7] So really, learning to switch off that inner chatter is a good investment.

Keep asking yourself: Do you need the focused attention or the receptive one? Will judging thoughts be useful, or would you rather observe and sense more strongly so that you can gain access to more information flowing from your surroundings? Note the effect of your choices and flexibility going from one thing to the other. Your mindset will have both emotional and bodily effects (⇨ EMOTIONS, BODY).

The power of optimism

Optimists perform better — as long as they are not *too* optimistic! Research shows that if you evaluate yourself as being slightly better than you currently are, you are likely to approach tasks in a more positive way, put more effort into your work, be more persistent, experience less stress, and perform better.[8] Conversely, if you think, "This is as far as I can go — and no further," you will not go any further. It is possible to limit your ability to perform through your thoughts.

> **If you evaluate yourself as being slightly better than you are, you perform better!**

Understandably, in cases where there is a lot at stake, or where there is significant risk of causing accidents, this kind of thinking is reasonable. In all other situations, however, you reduce the optimism that is the driving force behind your continued development and great results (⇨ SUCCESSES).

The key word here is "self-efficacy"— the belief that you can get results, attain goals, and achieve success in specific situations. Self-efficacy is about being able to evaluate your performance at three different points in time — before, during, and after:

- *Before-thinking* should ideally aim a bit too high. When you are forced to stretch in order to reach something, your motivation increases. A job should be hard enough to be interesting, but not so hard as to be impossible.

- *Thinking-in-action*, which takes place during the process itself, closely involves the "receptive attention" we have already touched upon. It is a learning process where the boundary between the inner and the outer is eliminated.[9]

- *After-thinking* is the thoughtful evaluation of a process, and it is a way of thinking that raises relevant questions for your continued development.

But be aware that being "optimistic" and trusting the good results is different from being "positive." Many people seem to equate the two. Being positive has to do with approving the situations, circumstances, people, etc., you happen to be around. Quite a few people seem to have decided to be positive, no matter what, but positive judgments are judgmental too and can trap you.

It is important to know the difference between compliments (positive judgments), corrections (negative judgments), and observations. When you are able to tell the difference, your sense of awareness improves, and you become able to evaluate how much time you actually use in either of those modes.

Compliments are expressions of *outer* motivation; outer motivation can stifle *inner* motivation, which is the true driving force of self-development. Inner motivation is when you do something because you "just cannot help it." One of the noticeable indicators of personal growth is the development of a stronger inner motivation. You get to know your innermost self — and use this knowledge daily in your engagement with valuable goals (⇨ VALUES, GOALS, SUCCESSES).

> **Outer motivation can stifle inner motivation — the true driving force of self-development.**

When it comes to your thought processes, one of the most useful ways to use optimism is to learn from situations. No matter the situation there is always something useful to be learnt. Asking appropriate and constructive questions can fuel your journey and give you the experience of leading a life full of learning. These are some useful questions to ask yourself along the "Learner's Path"[10]:

- What is the learning for me in this?
- Which values were at stake here — for the other person(s), and for me?
- How can I apply my learning?
- What is now possible?

Now that you know the difference between various approaches in your thinking, try to assume a "helicopter perspective" whenever you need a really fresh view of things (⇨ PERCEPTION). This is where you look down upon something that is happening with inquisitive, learning-oriented questions at the back of your mind, for instance "What patterns do I notice?" Or, if you were to look down on your life, and assign a percentage (100 per cent in total) to the time that you spend in each of these four different approaches, what would your distribution look like?

- ◉ Negatively judging — ( ) per cent
- ◉ Positively judging — ( ) per cent
- ◉ Observing — ( ) per cent
- ◉ Learning-oriented — ( ) per cent

What does this distribution mean to your life? Which aspects of your life does it hinder? Which does it further? What changes to your current distribution would be relevant and useful?

From rocking chair to the Circle of Influence

There are several dead-ends that your thought processes can lead you into. Two of the most common ones are worrying and complaining.

Worrying begins and grows when you deal with something that you are not in control of, or that you are not doing anything about. Perhaps you are a little depressed, and you begin to worry about what could be wrong. Things usually go from bad to worse; sad thoughts lead to negative framings and emotions, which make everything look grey. But worrying is often directed at something in the future that cannot be predicted: "I wonder, will I get seriously ill (again)?" "What if I get fired?" "Are we going to crash?" Like the humorist Erma Bombeck said, "Worry is like a rocking chair: it gives you something to do, but it doesn't get you anywhere." A study at Yale and Pennsylvania State University has showed that five minutes of worry is enough to put you in a bad mood.[11]

Five minutes of worry is enough to put you in a bad mood.

Complaining is dealing negatively with something. It could be your situation, other people, the weather — anything. You open your mouth, and out flies a negative statement. You are discontented and you let it all out. A Danish study[12] showed that

complaining is the leading cause of irritation at work; it is plainly and simply what bothers us the most about our co-workers.

Consider this example: At the call centre at a municipal office, there was a particularly bad vibe among the staff. It turned out that a group of them — led by a female employee, Sandy — were unhappy that some of their colleagues generally logged onto the telephones too late. The system made it possible for all to see when others logged in — did it happen at 8:57, 9:00, or 9:08? In describing her indignation, Sandy worked herself up to the verge of exploding. After a few hours of dialogue, the group assigned themselves the task of being punctual in the period leading up to the next meeting, two weeks later. The group would document their results day by day. Everyone bought into this experiment. When the next meeting took place, the group was able to show excellent numbers for when they had logged on. But Sandy was still as angry as a bull. "Now we have done what you wanted for so long," said one of the others. "Yes," she replied, "but now I am mad about something else!"

The above demonstrates the nature of complaining: if it's not one thing that's wrong, then it's another. The real problem is not what the complainer wants changed — that is merely the symptom. If that is changed, the complainer finds something else to be unhappy about. Complaining is primarily an inner condition that finds an outlet wherever available. It can be extremely frustrating for the people around to try to accommodate the complainer's demands, only to see the same negative energy surface elsewhere.

When working with your thoughts it is helpful to keep in mind Stephen Covey's distinction between the "Circle of Interest" and the "Circle of Influence."[13] The Circle of Interest encompasses those things you are interested in and worry about, while the Circle of Influence encompasses those things you can directly do something about and have influence on:

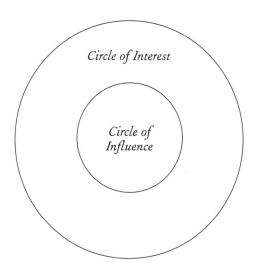

The distinction is in line with the so-called "Serenity Prayer": "God, grant me the serenity to accept the things I cannot change, courage to change the things I can, and wisdom to know the difference." In other words, you can change some things but not all. The art lies in knowing the difference — and putting your energy into the things that you can actually influence.

Pass me the remote control, please!

At the outset, many people who pursue change want to change things in their Circle of Interest: an annoying co-worker, a partner they would like to act differently, a promotion they want to take place. "Pass me the remote control, please!" seems to be their state of mind. This way of thinking takes place within the

Circle of Interest, and leads to an inner experience characterised by dissatisfaction and helplessness.

Researchers know that you can actually *learn* helplessness, and that it is one of the primary causes of sadness, stress, and depression.[14] Humans (and animals) can learn over time to react helplessly in unpleasant situations, even though they actually have the power to change that situation.

A series of thought-provoking experiments, led by the psychologist Martin Seligman, have shown the clear and persistent effects that the feeling of helplessness leaves on the psyche. A number of dogs were put into cubicles, one by one, and periodically subjected to physically non-damaging but painful electric shocks. The dogs in one group were able to stop the shocks by moving their heads — they experienced that they could influence their own situations. The dogs in the other group could not affect the unpleasant shocks. The next phase of the experiment tested what the dogs had learnt and how they would apply that learning. They were now put in larger boxes that were sub-divided by a low wall into two compartments. One compartment still delivered the electric shocks, the other did not. The dogs were put in in pairs — one had been able to exercise control in the first phase of the experiment, the other had not. The dogs used to exercising control over their own situation soon figured out how to jump over the low partition to escape the shocks. But of the dogs that had not been able to end their initial shocks, two-thirds lay passively on the floor and suffered — even though clear role models were present. Although the dogs whined, they made no attempts at escaping. The helplessness experienced in the first phase of the experiment had made a lasting impression on the

Helplessness is one of the primary causes of sadness, stress and depression.

dogs, which they carried with them to their new situation.[15]

Similar experiments with people show similar results. In one such experiment, test subjects had to perform assignments while exposed to an annoying sound. The experiment showed that when a person was given the possibility of shutting off the sound, his performance improved — even though he rarely took advantage of the possibility. The researchers, Seligman and Donald Hiroto, explained that simply acknowledging one's ability to exert influence is enough to counteract a distracting noise.

In other words, whether you think you have an influence over a situation makes a world of difference to your emotions and performance. What examples of this can you identify in your own life? Learn to constantly filter the world in relation to what you can influence and what you cannot influence. That will help you prioritise how you spend your time and energy. Those who search for things they can influence shall find things they can influence.

As Victor Frankl, a World War II concentration camp survivor, came to realise during his experiences, we can always influence how we think about things. He called it "the last freedom of man": "to choose your attitude to any situation; to choose your own path"[16] (⇨ PERCEPTION).

When people, dogs, or other animals suffer from behavioural passivity and helplessness, two things happen in the brain: the amygdala, the alarm bell of the brain, is activated; at the same time, the activity in the left prefrontal cortex — responsible for our motivation and positive feelings — decreases. The experience of being able to influence your situation is thus closely woven together with your well-being: I can act in meaningful ways, therefore I am.

Take a moment now to reflect upon which of the following are

situated within your Circle of Interest, and which belong to your Circle of Influence:

- Delayed flight departure
- Market conditions
- Your circadian rhythm
- What others think about you
- Fashion
- Your social circle
- Cuts in the departmental budget
- Other people's weaknesses
- Your upbringing
- Global warming

Deciding which circle these phenomena belong in is not easy; it's seldom black and white, and rather more dependent upon subjective experience and "framing" (⇨ PERCEPTION).

There is another tricky thing to bear in mind: Just because you can influence things, it does not necessarily mean that you choose to do so. You could influence, say, the local politics in your municipality if you wanted — but do you? You could positively influence your health by eating nutritious food, but do you? Your response and choices depend on your values and subjective interpretation of those values (⇨ VALUES).

Be aware, too, of the difference between "closed" questions (e.g., "Can I influence my own situation?") that call for a yes/no answer, and "open" questions (e.g., "What can I influence in this situation?") that allow for and encourage a more elaborated and nuanced answer.

Improving the quality of your questions

In tracing your thoughts, try writing down your inner dialogue. This allows you to externalise your thoughts and see your thought patterns from outside. You will get to know your thinking habits, probably have a good laugh over them, and you can then decide to put some new ones into practice. Seeing your thoughts written down makes it is so much easier to differentiate what works well and what works less well. The distance and neutrality of emotion helps our clear-sightedness, and paves the way for insights.

You could start in front of your computer, writing down whatever thoughts enter your mind. Listen to your inner voice. Keep writing. Look at it afterwards. If your inner dialogue is not particularly constructive, don't be disheartened. Look at it from the outside, from the "helicopter perspective," as an objective bystander would. And do remember your sense of humour — you will need it! Most inner dialogue goes around in circles, like one of those old LPs stuck in a groove. It ends up being so predictable that it is actually laughable.

Most inner dialogue goes around in circles, like an old LP stuck in a groove.

When you start listening to the questions that roam inside you, you realise where your general focus is. Different kinds of questions contribute differently to your reflective process. What do your questions sound like? What is the quality of your thoughts currently? To what extent do they help you and your surroundings towards optimism, happiness, self-efficacy, and the belief that things can succeed? To what extent are they like a nail in your tyre that makes the air slowly seep out — thereby draining its ability and power to do what it is good at?

Listen out for your balance of closed versus open questions.[17] Some people almost never ask anything but closed questions, and rely on the other person's willingness to elaborate a longer answer from that. "Are you happy?" is a question that invites a

yes/no response. An open formulation could be, "How are you feeling right now?" "You are smiling — what is it like to be you right now?" The last open question is based on your observation of the person's body language. It is also called "global listening."[18] Notice how the open questions elicit nuanced replies, which the other person formulates based on his unique "maps" (⇨ PERCEPTION).

Sometimes, closed questions can be leading, and thus decisive. A participant of a coaching course coached another participant on the latter's relationship with his boss. The coach ended up asking, "Can you see any possibility at all of the relationship improving?" The coachee answered, "No," and the coach instantly knew that he had gotten it wrong. When the coachee showed up for the next module, he had changed his job — and boss.

We are co-creators of one another's reality through our questions. We shape each other's perceived choices as well as our own. That is why it is so important that you become conscious of your language. You are the master of your own thoughts, questions, and inner dialogue. To a very large extent, you create your own reality through the things you focus on. What you focus on, you nourish. What you nourish, grows. What grows, becomes your reality.

Metaphorically speaking, you have a torch inside your brain. What you shine it on is what you pay attention to. There is something in the cone of light, but there is also always a lot that's hidden. Every time you have a thought, you select something and reject a whole lot of other options. Asking constructive questions is a choice — and the good news is that it can be turned into a habit.

> **You have a torch in your brain: what you shine it on is what you pay attention to.**

On such a road to change, bear in mind how change is created neurally. You want to strengthen the useful connections in your brain — make them stronger and more "hard-wired." These connections may right now only be invisible paths in the forest, but by walking them more often, you can make them deeper, more visible, and easier to travel (⇨ PERCEPTION). Equally, don't dwell too much on your "mistakes" along the way. You may find that you ask lots of closed questions or that you are in "Judger" mode quite often. Note this, and then let go of it by focusing on where you want to go, combined with a mindful presence in a body at ease (⇨ GOALS, BODY). Paying a lot of attention to your mistakes will in fact only strengthen them — and make change more difficult — because the brain has thus been turned into an opponent.

It is also one of the reasons why adopting a musical mindset is so important — because being flexible, playful, and resilient helps you stay on track, and get back on track if you depart from the desired route.

Tramp your new path as often as you can — and when you make mistakes, you may as well turn them into friendly reminders of the path you want to walk. You are likely to make many mistakes along the way, so make the most of them. Return to your desired path gracefully and continue travelling on this new path. The brain will help you in creating this change because you are now respecting its logic.

But if you find yourself leaving the path you have defined for yourself time and again, you may need to play your other keys in order to learn more about your underlying drive and dedication (⇨ VALUES, GOALS). It may be that you — or others — have defined a path, a goal, or a practice that really isn't that important, relevant, attractive or appropriately formulated. Often a slight twist of path will make a huge big difference.

Ask yourself honest questions — they will awaken your inner motivation and initiative. Take, for example, the open question, "Who can help me?" It is constructive in an entirely different way from its closed counterpart, "Is there anyone who can help me?" Take a moment now to experience the difference between closed and open formulations:

Closed: Have you had success with anything similar before?
Open: What have you had success with in similar situations?

Closed: Do you have any options?
Open: What options do you have?

Closed: Can you handle the task?
Open: Which resources do you need to draw upon now?

It is very important that you master the difference, in order to liberate and strengthen the play on your inner piano. Through self-regulation — asking more curious, open questions, but also some closed ones at times when you are seeking particular information ("Is this the route to the hospital?") — you will be able to upgrade your general communication quality.

Open questions are often signalled by "Wh-" words — what, which, when, etc. It may be beneficial, however, to avoid the question "Why?" "Why" can easily sound accusatory, and make people (or yourself) defensive: "Why haven't you done anything about it yet?" Constructive alternative questions could be:

- ⊚ What did you give priority to instead? Which of your values did you thereby honour?
- ⊚ When did you come closest to doing something about it?
- ⊚ What would be a useful first step to get you started?

Notice how potential blame here turns into curiosity through the play on the Values, Successes, and Goals keys.

Playing the Thoughts key

When playing the Thoughts key, remember how musicians also sometimes go out of tune. What do they do then? Give up? Start blaming themselves? If the latter, they are sure to make more mistakes. Instead, good musicians focus on getting back on track. It may take a note or two or more. It may take a spot of improvisation. But they know where they are going and they're going to get there. By adopting a musical mindset you strengthen your resilience.

How do you apply this when playing the Thoughts key?

- When you find yourself being self-judgmental, ask yourself how useful that is. If it is not useful, start observing things instead, being neutral in what you notice. Put into words what you see, so that you may ensure that you stay in the role of the impartial observer, registering "what is," nothing else.

- When you find yourself lost in inner dialogue, ask yourself whether you need that at that moment — or whether you may actually gain from a more spacious awareness of what is going on. What would a switch from "focused attention" to "receptive attention" give you?

- When you find yourself asking closed questions, ask yourself how useful they are for your present task. Closed questions are good if you want to get particular information out of someone. But they do not lead to much constructive reflection. If those closed questions are not the best choice right now, change to open questions.

- When you find yourself feeling low, or worried, or anxious, ask yourself if and how you can actually influence the matter. Then gently move your attention from your Circle of Interest to your Circle of Influence.

The art here is to switch elegantly and flexibly. Some people are in the habit of "self-complaining" if they do something wrong. The musical mindset will help you get going and keep your spirits high. The experience of "noticing — changing focus — continuing" is a bit like a pendulum: it swings, changes direction, swings again in a slightly different way. It is a bodily experienced musicality that you best of all start experimenting with yourself, so that you get to know the state little by little and become increasingly confident of your ability to return to it again and again.

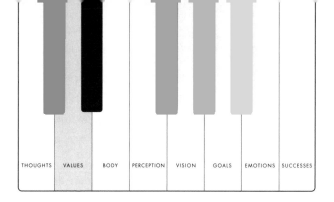

| THOUGHTS | VALUES | BODY | PERCEPTION | VISION | GOALS | EMOTIONS | SUCCESSES |

2

Values

Appreciating the core of interplay

WE ALL HAVE some things that we treasure more than others, things we would like to see more of in the world. These are our values, and though surprisingly unexplored by many, they are truly the heartbeat of human existence and interplay. In music, values have to do with the particular qualities you wish to emphasise and enhance. But, even two musicians who agree that a piece of music should be played, say, "longingly," will have very different understandings of what that means in practice. The more we understand ourselves and others in terms of values, the deeper we can connect to one another, the stronger we can communicate, and the more we can contribute relevantly to the world we all live in. This chapter will help you do so.

What are your values? Perhaps you have a clear picture of

them. But, if you are like most people, your understanding of what is truly important in your life will be less clear. Many people wait until late in life to explore and put into words what really matters to them. "I cannot believe it has taken me so long to get to know myself," they say with surprise.

Your values make up the core of who you are and what you do. Without them, you would not be you. Values represent everything that is fundamentally important to you. As you become aware of them, they act as your "guiding stars" in life, helping you decide what to spend your time and energy doing and thinking. Values motivate you to take action.

Values and action are twins; they go hand in hand. If you want to be something that you currently are not, this is an "ideal," not a "value." Constantly mirroring your values in your actions and your actions in your values is an important part of getting to know and working with your values.

"Walk the talk" is a popular management expression inspired by this. It means that you do what you say you are doing; that your actions and words match; that you are trustworthy and congruent.

Since values are closely related to action, it is important to ask yourself how visibly your values show in your behaviour. The career man may say that

Constantly mirror your values in your actions, and your actions in your values.

"respect" and "family" are core values in his life, but if a film crew followed him and his family's busy daily lives over the next months, is this what they would see? Or would they conclude that these were not his values, but rather his ideals, disconnected from the life he leads?

The next pages invite you to embark on an exciting journey.

36

Many people say that exploring their values has been among the most powerful exercises they have ever gone through; that it marked a turning point for them. No matter your level of experience with values, this is a key you will gain from by playing more often and more fluently.

Know your core values

It is useful to know your core values — but it is not always easy to identify them. The seven exercises below will help you explore your values from several angles.

A few notes before you begin. In these exercises, there are no right or wrong answers. No values are "better" than others. Be attentive to how you define your values — your meaning of your value words may not be exactly the same as how the dictionary (or another person) defines it. Be honest when you do the exercises — your platform for achieving great results will be stronger that way. View your list as work in progress, a draft to constantly refine, instead of something absolute or final. Most people experience, anyway, that their values — or at least their interpretation of their value words — change over life. This may be true of you too. Finally, it is a good idea to take notes for each exercise. Better still, draw a mind-map with your most important values represented in bubbles and connected to one another with lines. This is how the brain works — with associations. In the end, you will have a rich picture of your values; see how they connect, and then you can prioritise which are the most important ones to you.

1. Turning points

What turning points have you experienced in your life? What powerful moments have had a decisive impact on you?

You may want to imagine your life as a path, and then identify

the passages where the path twisted and changed direction. These twists may have been caused by an important realisation, a friendship, the death of a loved one, a change of job, and so on.

The turning points in your life are not just the things that made an impression, or even a lasting impression for that matter. Your turning points are the experiences that changed you deeply, maybe even spiritually. They may have created an experience of "no way back."

When you have identified your turning points, ask yourself what they have done to you. Which values have grown from those experiences? Which of your values have been strengthened through these experiences? Which have been challenged? Which have changed?

2. Highlights

The highlights in your life, as opposed to turning points, are the ecstatic moments or periods during which you were extremely consumed by something, to the disregard of time and place. You may have faced challenges, but you still felt on top of the situation. It could have been a single moment of happiness, or an experience that lasted anywhere from hours to days, characterised by intense joy, inner clarity, tranquillity, and/or "flow" experiences."[1] "Flow" is achieved, according to the psychologist Mihaly Csíkszentmihályi, when there is perfect harmony between your challenges or tasks and your ability to tackle them.[2]

> "Flow" is perfect harmony between the challenges you face and your ability to tackle them.

Choose a number of highlights from your life and reflect on what excited you about the experience, and which values you thus honoured.

3. Anger triggers

When you value something, you are likely to shun its opposite.[3] If you value, say, freedom, you become frustrated, angry or sad, when freedom is restricted. When you find yourself in a situation that seem to trigger such emotions, then it is likely there is something in that situation — or something that the people in the situation do — that conflicts with one or more of your values. (However, be alert to the possibility that the anger and frustration may be coming about by habit, or because you are seeing something in others that you do not like in yourself!)

Now, think back on a number of relevant situations. Which of your values were challenged or trampled here? Which actions were inhibited? What were you unable to accept in that situation? What does it say about your values?

4. Compliments

Compliments are expressions of recognition, of what others particularly appreciate about you. Which are the best compliments you have ever received? What is the best compliment that your partner/spouse/friend/boss/client or a stranger could possibly give you? What does the fact that you regard these compliments as the "best" ones tell you about what you value in life?

5. Value transmission

Which values would you most like to pass on to other people you care about? If you were to cut to the chase, what specific difference would you most like to make in this world? What would you like to be written on your tombstone? What do you want to be remembered by future generations for? What is so important to you that you would give up a lot to make it happen? Do you have anything or anyone that you are ready to die for? What or

who is it? While doing this exercise, which values of yours are you reminded of?

6. Needs

Human beings are not islands; we are connected to one another by something valuable — but what is it? What must be a part of the way you live your life, so that you can be the person you are? Who must be a part of the way you live your life, so that you can be the person you are? How must you live your life, irrespective of what others say or do? What is sacred to you? What makes you feel, "This is truly me"? What is the common thread in your life?

7. Beliefs

What do you believe to be true about life? Do you have any mottos? If yes, what are they? If no, which mottos would encapsulate the way you live and prioritise? Which sayings and quotations do you really like? What do these say about you and your values?

Summary: Your values

Now that you have worked through the seven-step value exercise, you can run through your notes and search for patterns. You may want to imagine that you are flying in a helicopter (that you have gone "meta" ⇨PERCEPTION) and that you are looking down at your notes from a distance: What stands out? What do you notice? Which insights provoked strong emotions? Which values do you recognise across the different exercises?

Make a "clean" list now of the values identified, that is, with just single words or short sentences that encapsulate who you are, without the stories and notes you have jotted done in the process.

From value words to behavioural evidence

When values are at the centre of attention, so are beliefs. Your beliefs consist of the things that seem real and enlightening to you, the way things ought to be (⇨ PERCEPTION); they determine, to a large extent, how you cope with life, what you notice, and what meanings you attribute to things.

Whenever a value is mentioned, particular behavioural assets are subjectively attributed to it. We talk about "value words" versus "behavioural evidence." To everyone a particular behaviour expresses certain values. And a particular value word becomes real through the behaviours we associate with it. However, because human beings differ significantly in how we think and attribute meaning to situations, we do not agree on these things. What may be triggered in, say, your colleague's mind when he or she hears the word "respect" is likely to be different — maybe even very different — from what is activated in your mind.

For this matter, differences between people can in fact be highly useful. Assuming we are open to other cultures, we tend to be more aware of and curious about differences in interpretations when we perceive another person as coming from a different culture. By contrast, when we interact with

Even when we think we agree on particular values, do we really?

a person who is perceived to be similar to us, say from the same culture, we often assume that we both know and agree on what we are talking about. But many misunderstandings are actually born out of this belief in "sameness."

Consider the concept of "mutual respect," which was recognised as a common value by one department in an organisation. During a meeting each member of the department was asked to describe what qualified as evidence of this "mutual respect."

41

Their responses varied considerably:

- When we follow the common procedures we agreed on.
- When we give people room to do things differently.
- When we talk nicely to one another.
- When we give one another honest feedback.
- When we show interest in and ask questions about one another's lives.
- When I am given space and silence to get my job done.

This is a great example of how we differ when it comes to the behavioural evidence we attribute to certain values. Different people have different "maps" in the brain.[4] Even when we think we agree on particular values, do we really?

Digging below the surface

You can be sure, however, that all maps and values are meaning-ful — even though it may not instantly be clear to you how. If you meet the world with curiosity and dare to ask questions in order to learn new things, you will understand the role of particular values and maps in other people's sense-making.

Some values seem to be popular. Many of us would agree par-tially or completely that these values are our values:

- Respect
- Freedom
- Trust
- Joy
- Independence

But this does not mean that we understand them the same way. "Freedom" would have a different meaning and different behavioural evidence to a politically liberal person than it does to someone with socialist beliefs; they represent two different forms of existence.

The value "curiosity" could be used by a person who is deeply interested in technical matters, and technical matters only, as well as by a person who is curious about human beings and their motives.

The value "independence" is likely to imply quite different actions espoused by someone from Asia as compared to someone from Europe.

We do not know what lies below the surface unless we dig deeper — and ask! And often we do not know ourselves; we are not aware of the different versions of values, and we seem to believe that if a person agrees to our value word, then he also agrees to its meaning.

But the peculiarities do not stop here. Let us now look at the behavioural level. A department in an organisation agrees on some rules regarding cooperation:

- We say good morning to one another.
- We respond to all emails within 24 hours.

Agreeing to follow the rules does not, however, mean that the employees respect and honour the same values while following the rules. Some may say it does not matter which values they honour — as long as they get the job done. But it does matter. We assume that we are "aligned" when we have agreed on something behaviourally. However, when misunderstandings and conflicts arise, we realise that it was an illusion.

Perhaps one person might follow the above rules out of a sense of "duty" or "loyalty" to the rules; another one might be honouring his value of "service"; a third might be focusing on the value of "positivity." This does not necessarily lead to problems, but it may. And the energy that the employees approach a task with — depending on their framing — would in any case be completely different (⇨ PERCEPTION).

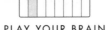

A lot of self-insight — and a greater understanding and acceptance of others — is generated when one first sees the connections between values and behavioural evidence. The next time you come across someone you do not immediately understand, you may find it useful to ask: "Which values is he or she honouring now?" If you want to get to know a person (or yourself) better, be curious about the relationships between their core values and their behavioural evidence.

Value tensions are like magnets

Values are stable but, at the same time, they are dynamic. This may sound like a paradox, but it makes sense. Values are always in use, and in interplay with your experiences. Some values wane over the course of your life; others increase in importance. You may also experience that your behavioural evidence of a value changes: what you considered behavioural evidence of "freedom" as a 16-year-old would hardly be the same as when you are 65.

The most fundamental tension in the brain resembles the two poles of a magnet: attraction and repulsion. When you are particularly attracted towards one value or opinion, you are simultaneously repelled by what you perceive to be its opposite.

Behavioural evidence of a value is not just one-sided and decided upon once and for all. We may like or love certain "versions" of something, but feel repelled when we think about or experience other versions of it. Maybe you love practising "freedom" in your life in terms of freedom of speech, but would not dream of practising it in terms of freedom to climb the toughest mountains in the world. For some, "freedom" is a marriage full of trust and love; for others, "freedom" is never getting married.

Your take on values and their behavioural evidences may

change across time and circumstance, which only adds to the complexity and fascination.

The dynamic quality of your values is caused, in part, by these value tensions.[5] It can therefore be useful to look at values in pairs, since the choice of one value consciously or unconsciously assumes the exclusion of the opposite value.

You can observe this at a very basic level: When you spot a dangerous snake, you react instantly and avoid it; when you see a person you really like, you instantly go straight to them. Evolution has equipped us with the ability to move between these two extremes — *away from* and *towards* — which you, to a large degree, can learn to consciously control from the frontal lobes in your brain.

However, they also work subconsciously in the deeper areas of the brain — the amygdala and hippocampus. The right brain hemisphere is the magnetic pole that makes us withdraw from something, while the left brain hemisphere makes us approach it inquisitively. If someone suffers from depression, the left hemisphere is suppressed and the right side takes the lead; the person closes up, withdraws, and grinds to a halt. If, on the other hand, the right hemisphere is damaged, this results in the person becoming highly agitated, being interested in everything, and thinking that he has never felt this good before. In the same way, positive stimuli promote openness because they affect the left hemisphere, while negative impulses promote the right hemisphere's tendency to close us off.

The right brain hemisphere makes us withdraw from something, the left makes us approach it.

This state of tension makes values dynamic, and makes our existence exciting. However, be very attentive to the goal of working with value tension: to gain insight into some of the

components that make up a "map," be it your own or someone else's. The goal is not to create rigid thinking that is limited to black and white or either/or — which renders us blind to all the colourful nuances that exist in between, and fools us into believing that there is only one true "anti-value" for each value.

There are value words you are attracted towards, and some you are repelled by. But bear in mind that a value word you do not like may taste the way it does because it triggers particular connotations in you. For another person that very value word may trigger something completely different. Which means that you do not only make a choice at the level of value words, you also choose at the level of behavioural evidence, including the beliefs linked to this.

An example: When you were young you might not have liked "tradition" because you associated it with having to repeat the same odd rituals again and again. You linked it to "conformity" and "superficiality," and would much rather see "innovation" or a "creativity." However, as you grew older, you came to realise

Make way for change by changing your associations.

that tradition carried important meaning and that you could create your own traditions — bringing life to events that lit up the eyes of your loved ones; something they looked forward to participating in. In that respect, you proactively moved "tradition" into your Circle of Influence (⇨THOUGHTS), and it started resembling "fun," "room for initiative," and "creativity" to you.

This example shows how connotations can change. It also shows that what seemed to be a contradiction ("tradition" versus "innovation") resolved itself when it started seeming possible to create tradition *through* innovation — and to have fun while ensuring there was room for initiative for everyone involved. So basically, what happens here is that you make way for a change in your physical world by changing your associations in your mental world.

This, in fact, is the logic behind many things in human life: If your associations to something are negative and cause you to tense up or "shrink," you are not likely to want to proceed. If, however, your associations are optimistic, you are eager to move on; you are now in touch with your inner motivation (⇨ GOALS).

The value network of the brain

The brain's value system is a bridge between feelings and reason. It is a dynamic balance, which oscillates between certainty and uncertainty. Uncertainty may be an uncomfortable position, but, as Voltaire pointed out, certainty is an absurd one. The better you are at maintaining — and being satisfied in — these tensions, the higher your intelligence; and then you can juggle many balls in the air with a steady hand.

Values are not localised in any one area of the brain, but belong to an *integrated network*, one which brain researchers are in the process of exploring.[6] The figure on the next page illustrates the areas that are under particular observation; it is in this network that they are searching for answers regarding values as brain activities.

Each of the areas contributes in its own way to a collective image of how the brain works when we attribute values to thoughts and behaviour.

The anterior gyrus cinguli, which is a part of the frontal lobes in the brain, appears to be a monitoring system of the brain: it controls the interaction between the individual brain sections, and which weighs values relative to one another. It is therefore a system that can change the state of tension between the various

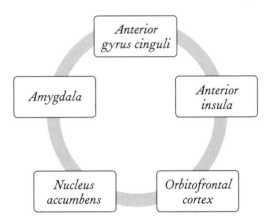

brain areas. The area is active when, for example, discrepancies arise between what we desire here and now and what we *should* be doing, or when we get an idea to doing something in a completely different way.

We often experience conflicts between short-term values and long-term ones, say, between eating the cream puff now and the advantage of being slim in the future. What happens is that the amygdala suddenly gets a craving for cream puffs, while the orbitofrontal cortex[7] and the anterior insula insist on a more far-sighted health strategy.

It is in this context that the anterior gyrus cinguli intervenes — to mediate.

The strategy that then wins the tension battle — let us assume that the amygdala wins the cream puff — activates the nucleus accumbens, located in the deeper regions of the brain; this releases dopamine, which rewards us with a state of well-being; we feel good and things seem meaningful to us. The nucleus accumbens motivates the action that gets the cream puff into the mouth, and gives us a short-term feeling of well-being, as well as strengthening the learning process that will increase the probability that the cream puff will win in the future. The cream puff has now been assigned a special value.

Thus, when there is a conflict between values, activity in the anterior gyrus cinguli increases; when the conflict is resolved, activity is generated in the areas of the brain that deal with rewards.

Slip sliding away

One thing leads to another (as you will also see in the Body key). Something we were not at all attracted to before — or thought possible then — can all of a sudden turn into an obvious attraction because one "yes" led to the next "yes" which led to the next "yes."

This point is extremely pertinent when we talk about values. A shocking example of one thing leading to another and the relativity of values is the experiment conducted in 1961 by the psychologist Stanley Milgram from Yale University.

Milgram wanted to study how much pain an ordinary person was willing to inflict on another, just because he was ordered to do so by a research leader. Test subjects were told that the experiment was going to investigate the effect of punishment on learning. Everyone would be paid irrespective of the outcome of the experiment, and the roles of student and teacher were to be determined at random. In reality, the student was always an actor, and the teacher was always a test subject — but the test subjects did not know this.

The student had to memorise ten words, and was punished whenever he or she could not remember them. The punishment for forgetting the word order was an increasingly stronger electrical shock, which the teacher (the test subject) actively

administered by pushing a button. The first shock started at 15 volts, and the thirteenth and final one was 450 volts — from "slight shock" to "danger, severe shock," as it said in writing, in plain sight of the test subject.

Before the experiment, 14 psychologists from Yale University had been asked to speculate how hypothetical test subjects would react in such a setup. The most pessimistic psychologist believed that 3 out of 100 would go "all the way"— from 15 to 450 volts. On average, the psychologists believed that 1.2 per cent would go all the way.[8]

As it turned out, in Milgram's experiment, the number of subjects who went all the way, administering 450 volts, was 26 out of 40 — a chilling 65 per cent.

The experiment is too extensive to be discussed in detail here, but it is extremely interesting, because it shows what happens when a premise changes.

Would you be able to deliver a 450-volt shock to hurt another person? You would most likely answer "no." But, in a different context, with different rules and goals, and when you have actually started, then one step leads to another. In human life there are some yeses that very easily lead to other yeses, which you would otherwise never have said "yes" to.

> One "yes" led to the next "yes" which led to the next "yes."

The sociologist Zygmunt Bauman talks of "sequential action": once you have said A, you allow yourself to say B, leaving responsibility to be fluid.[9]

Perception, values, thoughts, and the actions of the body are closely related to one another — and to the context. The Nobel-winner Herbert Simon compares the human mind to a pair of scissors.[10] One blade is our brain and the other blade is the specific environment that our brain operates in at a given moment. You cannot separate one from the other. If you want to understand people — and yourself — you have to look at both blades simultaneously.

Context greatly influences our morality, and the choices we make. Think for a moment of the extreme situations that humans can end up in, situations where they get in touch with sides of themselves they never knew existed. Here, the Body key may take over and act directed by the Vision and Goals keys, focusing on the value of "survival," downplaying other values that normally drive their lives.

Think of the air crash in the Andes in 1972, where 16 of the 45 passengers survived more than two months in the snow — by eating the dead bodies. The book that describes the months and challenges in the ice-cold mountains is an inescapable record of how morality and context, reflection and action, are closely connected.[11] It shows us, too, the importance of environment in how values are interpreted and put into practice.

Context greatly influences our morality and the choices we make.

Several of Milgram's test subjects were deeply affected by how they — *they* — could have agreed to go as far as they did in that situation. But, as Bauman points out, humans can be brought to this point if the situation requires it to a sufficient degree. The obedience of the accomplices in the Holocaust is an obedience that most of us would be capable of.[12]

Milgram's experiment also generated an "extreme level of nervous tension" in the test subjects; they were sweating, moving around in their chairs, shivering, fumbling, stuttering, and laughing nervously.[13] Their bodies were fully engaged in communicating their moral conflict. In other words, there is a close link

between your values and your body. Intuition speaks through the body; your body shows the value judgments you make. This connection between values, morals and body is also the reason why such things as lie detectors exist: the body tells.

How do you know when you are in the process of doing something that you do not wholeheartedly want to, where you experience a value conflict, where you are "incongruent"?[14] How well do you know your body as a messenger of your values? Where are your boundaries in regards to what you will agree to do?

Stop for a moment and consider how frighteningly easy it is to "cheat" our brains. Some cheat other people's brains with good intentions; others do it with bad intentions. How can you actively cheat yours in a good way?

You may want to reflect on this, not just now, but in general, because when you work with yourself and aim at change, you actively manipulate and retrain your brain. Therefore, you might as well be able to do it thoughtfully, and with the values that you believe in.

Playing the Values key

It makes sense to play the Values key often. Ask yourself:

- Which values do I honour with options x, y, and z?
- Which values may my partner/colleague/child be honouring right now? What is his/her behavioural evidence?
- What is important here (to me/us/the organisation)?
- Which values do I want to honour?
- To what extent do I make room for these values?
- When does an opposing value pop up to challenge me?
- What if this particular action, honouring this particular value, is not possible (i.e., it is not in the Circle of

Influence, ⇨THOUGHTS) — what else may be possible to do, honouring the same value?

The way that you understand beliefs and values is always connected to what you perceive to be their behavioural implications and consequences. It is important to be attentive to this connection; otherwise, all this will be limited to theoretical talk without context or practice.

In fact, dealing with values is likely to make you rise to the occasion in life. Values are not just words – they must be made operational. It is not enough to say what you would like to see encouraged in the world, and what you care about; you have to develop your understanding of how you are going to do it.

Whatever you define as your goals in life, and whatever actions you (may) want to put into practice, seek to connect them to the values you and others are honouring. This way, you avoid tunnel vision and you can see the context: "What makes the goal meaningful?" "Which values do I/we honour?"

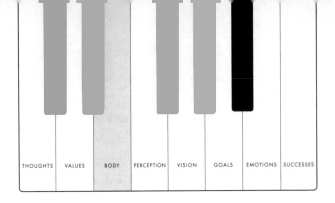

| THOUGHTS | VALUES | BODY | PERCEPTION | VISION | GOALS | EMOTIONS | SUCCESSES |

3

Body

Mastering your physical instrument

MUSIC IS GIVEN LIFE through the body. Singers train their voices to give power and nuance to their expressions; pianists, guitarists, drummers, all use not just their fingers and arms, but their entire bodies in making music. The rest of us use our bodies too — it constantly communicates and reveals much of those mental processes going on inside us. Bodily awareness and adeptness are at the very foundation of success. And often, only the slightest physical adjustment makes the difference between an ordinary performance and an extraordinary one. In this chapter, let us look at how to harness the power of our bodies to create the change we want.

The mind is anchored to the body

You have probably been through this: You catch the flu, and, while suffering the runny nose and body aches, promise yourself that, as soon as you get better, you will be grateful every day for the freedom and joy of a healthy body. How many days does that promise typically last? Yes, not very many!

Bodily well-being is one of those things that most of us take for granted. We take walks, run up the stairs, go shopping, drive our cars — all without being really aware of how the body works. It is often only when we are ill that we pay attention to our bodies.

But this is likely to change over the next few decades. Scientists now know that our bodies are the alpha and omega — everything begins and ends with the body. And scientists are now talking about "embodied cognition" — that is, the mind is inseparably anchored to the body's actions and surroundings.

In fact, "the brain cannot fully think about emotion without re-enacting, or physically simulating, that feeling."[1] When we read emotional words — like "anger," "bliss," "disgust" — and consider their meanings, the same subtle facial muscles are activated as when we actually experience the named emotions. Words associated with disgust, for example, cause us to curl our upper lips and wrinkle our noses. The purpose of this response, this flexing of muscles, seems to be to enable us to experience those emotions.

Thus is the body a core co-player in everything you do and say. It helps you understand your world, by mentally rehearsing what you see, hear and think about. And it colours your experience of the world — sitting on a hard chair, for instance, will make you a tougher negotiator, while sitting in a cosy room will arouse feelings of warmth within you.

55

Try this little exercise: Place both your hands on the table. Move one hand in circles; with the other, knock on the table. Do this for a few minutes. You will probably find it difficult, particularly at the beginning. Both hands would rather perform the same motion. But practice makes perfect. In the same way that we can steer the car, keep track of the flow of traffic, and listen to the radio all at once, we can train our hands' movements to the point where coordination becomes easy.

When we perform exercises like this one, we are initially aware of each movement. And we can describe the movements using language. But, when they become automatic, the body just performs them and we lose our awareness of each individual step. Later on, it can even be difficult for us to verbally explain what we are doing. Your feet may be really good at driving a car, but if you were asked, while doing something else, to name the order of the three pedals, you might not be able to say for sure!

Move powerfully from the slow "I ability" to the fast "me ability."

What has happened is that we have moved powerfully from the slow "I ability" (explicit knowledge) to the fast "me ability" (tacit knowledge).

There are many things in your life that your body "just does" — tacitly. If you are sitting in your chair doing Sudoku, you are probably not aware that your body is working eagerly. But it is! Put up a video camera and you will discover just how much. You could also ask your children or spouse to imitate you — it will make you laugh for sure.

The habits we have in life — the automatic processes — influence about 95 per cent of our thoughts, feelings, and behavioural patterns. And most of them have a clear bodily component. Your morning grooming habits. Your route to work. The way you react when someone "steps on your toes." Your shopping habits. Your work routines. Your posture and breathing patterns. Your body is a part of everything — what you do today, and what you want to create tomorrow.

Because your body "just does" so much in your life, it is important that you learn to feel it, to interpret it, to adjust it, and to use it appropriately. You have to make it a co-creator of your vision — the development that you want to turn into reality (⇨ VISION).

The online/offline body

We do not just *have* a body, we *are* a body. It is an inextricable part of our personalities, the very foundation of our emotions and thoughts. Even abstract thinking builds upon bodily experience.

When you go for a walk, you use your body to find the way. Your body tells you what is right, left, up, down. Your memory is based on bodily thinking: you remember best the events where your senses were particularly stimulated. When you tell others about an activity you did, such as going for a long run, in recounting and retelling it you think in movements.

Now, imagine a bowl of oranges placed on a table, and imagine yourself taking one. If your brain was scanned right now, the region corresponding to your hand would show activity — even though you are not actually moving your hand. Your body is participating in the thought, even though it is "offline." If you move your hand physically, it goes "online."

So if you want to change your habits, beliefs and behaviours — and this is presumably why you are reading this book — you need to observe your body and all its tacit knowledge.

Often, a little bit of fine-tuning of the body is enough to make a big difference: start looking people in the eyes; keep your back

straight; relax your facial muscles. Many of the useful tools that you can learn — and much of the empowering mindset you can build up — will be of little use if the body is not a core participant.

A classic example of this is your breathing. For example, consider a leader who has a very strict inner judge (⇨ THOUGHTS) and

Your breathing patterns can be an unidentified, constant opponent.

who, in difficult situations, quickly becomes nervous. She learns to coach herself to adopt a more constructive approach and to mentally rehearse how to handle demanding situations. All well and good. But, if she — like many others — breathes superficially, she will only be able to implement a fraction of this new mindset. Her breathing patterns will be an unidentified, constant opponent.

Shallow breathing patterns severely hinder our ability to concentrate. When we get nervous, our breathing tends to get shallower, anyway. And if we have poor breathing habits even before the nervous state sets in, we will not have much extra capacity to "draw upon"; so just at the time when we need more oxygen in the situation, we can't access it, because we have not learnt how.

If you are often short of breath, and breathe in such a way that your chest and shoulders move up and down, then a nervous version of your body will easily knock you out. If, on the other hand, you have deep breathing patterns, then you will have plenty to draw upon in demanding circumstances. Our lungs are huge reservoirs of resourcefulness, calm, and balance — but their power is only activated when we inhale deeply into our lower abdomen, in a slow, regular rhythm.

Observe your own breathing. Place one hand on your chest and one hand on your stomach. Where do you currently have the most movement? And when are you most successful at getting the air deep down in your abdomen? What do you do exactly? How does it feel inside? Look in the mirror. Ask others. Though it may take some practice, and some help, good breathing technique can definitely be learned.

You cannot just *decide* to be happy

A happy person's world is vastly different from an unhappy person's. The happy person has cheerful and optimistic thoughts, which are manifested in a straight back, a smiling face, and a daily life full of exciting bodily challenges and pleasant experiences. Extremely good experiences, we say, "go straight to the heart"; they are the body. The unhappy person, on the other hand, has sad thoughts, a hunched body, and a serious face, since life is literally depressing and grey.

How do you become the happy person? The gearshift that can change your mental state is found in the body's actions.

Some people seem to think that you can command yourself into happiness. "Cheer up," they exhort themselves. "Be happy!" "Stay positive!" But that is an illusion. You cannot just *decide* to be happy. What you can do, though, is take note of what activities make you happy — and do more of them.

Take note of what activities make you happy — and do more of them!

The body acts, and happiness grows. As you will see in a minute, you can change your emotions and thought patterns by making some small adjustments to the body. And vice versa!

What is your state like when you watch the morning sun shine through your bedroom window? Do you jump out of bed, thinking of all the exciting events the day will bring? Perhaps another day, on waking, you find yourself instead in a state of laziness — and roll over so you can sleep some more.

States influence your behaviour but they are not unchange-able. A state is a choice. Throughout an ordinary day we go in and out of many states. A day for some may consist of, say, a sales presentation, a technical consultation, an interview, listening to a friend, and housework. It is useful to access different states in order to be at one's best during each individual task.

Know your state, change your state

A state is a snapshot of your physical and mental condition prior to performing an action, and is made up of three basic compo-nents, all of which you can actively manipulate:

- *Body*: Your body language, facial expressions, move-ments, and posture. Pay attention to even the smallest things: a certain weight distribution, a particular sensa-tion in the cheekbones, specific little movements.
- *Focus*: What you believe in, what you "know" is true in a given situation, what you notice and pay attention to.
- *Language*: What you say to yourself and what you say to others; your voice quality, your intonation, the speed at which you speak. Be attentive to nuances. Not every-one hears an actual voice in their minds; instead they have the feeling that they received a message; what is this message?

To better understand what a state is, try this: Walk around the room as though you are sad and worried. Do this for a minute, then stop. Next, walk around the room for another minute as though you have just fallen in love. Take note of your body pos-ture and movements, what you focus on and hold to be true, and what you say to yourself. (Try this exercise with other people too. Or ask someone to observe you.)

Describe the difference to yourself. How was it when you

were in the sad and worried state? What characterised your body? What were your beliefs and where was your focus? And what did you say to yourself (either out loud or in your mind)?

And how was it when you pretended to be in love? What characterised your body? What were your beliefs and where was your focus then? And what did you say to yourself?

You have now experimented with just how little is needed to change your state. A tiny adjustment — the way you hold your head when you walk, what you focus on, the tone of that inner voice of yours — makes a world of difference. This is thought-provoking, and more importantly, incredibly liberating. It is within your "Circle of Influence," i.e., what you can affect (⇨THOUGHTS), to change how you fundamentally feel (⇨EMOTIONS).

Access your optimal state

The three core aspects of states — body, focus and language — can be visualised in a pyramid. As the model below shows, all three components work together to produce a state:

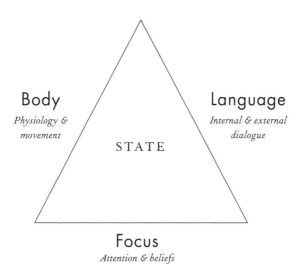

Body
Physiology & movement

Language
Internal & external dialogue

STATE

Focus
Attention & beliefs

The Pyramid of State is neither static nor universal: it varies from person to person, and from situation to situation. Understanding this pyramid model will allow you to manage your states, and access your optimal states.

Consider the case of a musician. If he suffers from performance anxiety, when he plays in front of an audience his performance will suffer by approximately 20 to 30 per cent. Some musicians in fact become so paralysed by the situation that they cannot perform at all. This is not because they are incompetent, but because they do not manage their state constructively. It would therefore be a good investment for the musician to train himself to understand his state when it is powerful and useful (his Pyramid of Success), and to understand his state when it is less useful (his Pyramid of Failure). The purpose of this is clear: to be able to activate the Pyramid of Success whenever needed.

An optimal Pyramid of Success for a musician might look like this:

Body

Erect posture

Even weight-distribution

Moves forward in a dynamic way

Deep, calm breathing

Open posture, shoulders back

Language

"Yes!"

"Now we're rolling!"

"I'm the king!"

"This is how music should sound."

"I'm in control of the game."

SUCCESS

Focus

Inner calm

One with the music

Everything is possible

BODY

A less useful state for a musician would look like this:

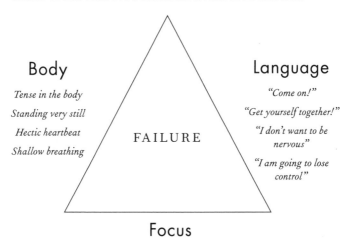

Body

Tense in the body
Standing very still
Hectic heartbeat
Shallow breathing

Language

"Come on!"
"Get yourself together!"
"I don't want to be nervous"
"I am going to lose control"

FAILURE

Focus

An exam! It's now or never!
Focused on inner dialogue
Diverted, not present

Speaking in terms of the eight keys of your inner piano, they are actively playing here. The three sides of the pyramid are represented by the Body key, the Thoughts key, and a combination of the Perception and the Values key. Your state very much shows in particular Emotions. You gain from identifying your Successes — successful states — so that you may access them while pursuing an important Goal. And you actively use your Vision to bridge the exercise here with the situations, events and challenges ahead.

This makes the Pyramid of Success an extremely powerful tool. Used to its fullest, you play all the keys one after the other and create a unique synergy. The order is up to you. Start with one key, play it for a bit. Change key when you feel that you have exhausted that key for the moment. Keep playing — see where it takes you!

Act! Use your body!

Looking at these very different pyramids for the same person, it becomes clear how you can use the same pyramid format to reflect upon your own optimal states for various situations. What characterises you in these situations? How does your body function? What do you say to yourself? What are you convinced is true in each situation? What grows because of your focus? It is important to recognise that your body holds a key to changing your state:

- You feel tired one evening and consider sitting down to watch TV. Instead, you go for a walk, and notice how it lifts your emotions, thoughts, and well-being.
- You are stuck in an assignment you are working on. You choose to do something else that is active — folding the laundry, tidying your desk — and you do it! You return to the assignment with new energy.
- You feel alone. You act on it — and you call someone who means a lot to you.

In other words: Act. Use your body. Do something else! There are two sets of key words here: "Do," which implies action, and "Something else," which is a consequence of your creativity. At the supermarket, for instance, instead of going down the aisle that tempts you, choose a different route. Instead of shopping while you're hungry, do it on a full stomach. Act! Try something slightly different. Feel how you grow when you seize power over your life in this way.

If what you do and say to yourself works and is appropriate, then keep doing it. If not, change strategy, do something else.

It is very effective to use the body to get in touch with your successful experiences (⇨ SUCCESSES). You can thus relive them and bring the resourcefulness to life again. Act as if you are calm, powerful, funny — or whatever your goal is — and you become calm, powerful, funny. The more you train, the stronger this ability becomes.

A child's entrance ticket into this world

Why do we yawn when others yawn? Why do older couples have the same facial expressions? How are children able to start learning the moment they are born? How is it that you can sometimes read other people's thoughts? The answer lies in *mirror neurons*.[2]

We sense intuitively that we can mirror ourselves in others. This is in fact a child's entrance ticket into this world. If you stick your tongue out in front of a baby, he will politely and joyfully return the gesture.[3] The child reads his mother's moods too: he can figure out what she is up to by following her eye movements and seeing what she rests her gaze on; if she smiles at something, it must surely be something pleasant; if she looks at a cup, the child quickly learns that she is about to give him something to drink.

Even though people have known this for millennia, it was only in 1996 that a group of researchers, led by the neurophysiologist Giacomo Rizzolatti, gave us a scientific explanation. They had discovered that in a specific region of the monkey's brain's frontal lobes, a group of nerve cells reacted whenever the monkey reached out for a piece of

The nerve cells also reacted when *other* monkeys reached out for the fruit.

fruit. The cells did not react when the monkey merely looked at the fruit but only when it actually reached out for it — even if it did so in total darkness. The intent manifested itself in the activity of the brain. But this was not all. The nerve cells also reacted when *other* monkeys reached out for the fruit. What the scientists

concluded, therefore, was that there are nerve cells in the brain that act like a mirror — that echo the environment and emulate what others do.

If the mother smiles, so does the baby; and yes, if we meet someone we do not know who smiles at us in passing we would be considered insensitive if we did not smile back. But, there are also people with less-developed mirror neurons, who have difficulty experiencing what is going on between people. They do not pick up all the signals that make everyday life pass smoothly, and they cannot intuitively predict what will happen. When this deficiency is particularly marked, as in autistic individuals, then social development grinds to a halt.

In the years since the monkeys revealed this secret, mirror neurons have been discovered in other areas of the brain. This raises some interesting questions about the boundaries of the self, when we are so extensively connected to others. It also questions the extent of our responsibility for each other's well-being, when our bad dispositions can so easily be transferred onto others, and when, equally, a positive remark can so swiftly lighten the mood between stressed colleagues (⇨ EMOTIONS).

Our mirror neurons reflect our environment — including the people around us — and add it to our behaviour. Without thinking about it, two brains that want to connect will tune in to the same frequency. Who am I facing? What opinions and emotions is this person broadcasting — and in what tempo, as the musician would ask? We seek out the wavelength with the best connection, in the same way you might search for the best reception on a tuner. There is just the crucial difference that we, as people, do not have a set frequency, but rather a variable one, which varies

Two brains that want to connect will tune in to the same frequency.

according to whom we are interacting with.

We have the ability to create good rapport and harmony, and we do this using the brain's *resonance system* (⇨EMOTIONS). This is also one of the musician's ways of connecting with his audience: the closer he is to his music, the better he is able to project its meaning.

When it comes to playing the Body key, the mirror neurons are crucial. If you understand their power, you may well choose to spend more time with people who excel at doing what *you* would like to be better at. By watching them, you already begin to train your brain to do similar things. It is a good idea, therefore, to look out for role models, and have the courage to ask them whether you may learn from their practice.

What the marshmallows teach us

At the beginning of the 1960s, the psychologist Walter Mischel performed an ingenious experiment with children — what has come to be known as the "marshmallow experiment."[4] He placed a marshmallow in front of each child and told him that the candy was his. "But," he added, "if you can hold off eating it until I come back from an errand, you will get another one."

A third of the children ate the marshmallow right away; a third waited 20 minutes to get another; the rest tried to wait but gave up along the way.

At the time of the experiment, the test subjects were four years old. Fourteen years later, when the first subjects had finished school, Mischel caught up with them, and reviewed their progress:

⊙ The children who had taken the marshmallow right
   away had lower self-esteem and more problems with
   their friends and acquaintances.

- ◉ Those who had waited for the second marshmallow, on the other hand, were more socially adept, self-assured, and academically competent.

There was thus a clear correlation between the "impulse control" or "delayed gratification" that subjects were able to demonstrate and their subsequent intellectual and social development.

The body's role here is crucial: Are you capable of taming and distracting it? Or, for that matter, to outdo it with will-based decisions? Self-control matures in the brain's frontal lobes. It's about postponing an immediate reward in favour of a greater one. It's about staying true to one value while being tempted by another — or several others (⇨ VALUES). Anyone with a sweet tooth who has had to say "No, thanks" to sweets during a diet knows this. It is something most people recognise: your body often wants something different from your will-based decisions.

When the slow and the fast systems work together in the brain, we can generate an act of will (⇨ VISION).[5] An act of will is based on self-control, on a concept of what you want to achieve, considerations about how you want to get there, a decision to carry out the action, and finally, sticking to the decision.

Consider how many goals are linked to bodily acts of will:

- ◉ I want to lose weight.
- ◉ I want to quit smoking.
- ◉ I want to run a marathon.
- ◉ I want to give others more time to speak at our meetings.
- ◉ I want to be the centre of attention.
- ◉ I want to be calm, not nervous.
- ◉ I want to be better at organising my time.
- ◉ I want to improve my relations with others.
- ◉ I want to make ten sales calls a day.

The body is a part of everything. That's why it's so important that you know it well. What is it saying? How does it feel? What does it look like?

To increase your knowledge of your body, you can start by improving your "mindfulness." Mindfulness is a conditioned mental state characterised by a calm awareness of your body's functions, thoughts, and emotions. It is the ability to see things exactly as they are, moment by moment. Instead of becoming preoccupied with a thought or an emotion, a mindful awareness calmly observes these thoughts and emotions as they come and go. It has to do with not getting attached to, say, a disturbance, but just letting it flow on.[6] While mindful, you are in the "pure" experience of the present, and you have an "inquisitive, open, and accepting" attitude towards this experience.[7] This is a very powerful state to be in on the path towards success.

Mindfulness is the calm awareness of your body's functions, thoughts and emotions.

Stress — the bad and the good

Stress prepares you to perform. Stress is a prerequisite for all learning.

These may not be the things you usually hear about stress. In the media, the word "stress" is associated with pessimism, depression, the struggle to survive, and being in a high-risk zone.

But there is also a good side to stress. Stress is an *adaptive mechanism*, which adapts your behaviour to the challenges in your surroundings. Adaptive behaviour draws upon two strategies — a primary strategy and a secondary strategy:

- The *primary strategy* is used by your brain when there a solution in sight.

ie *secondary strategy* is used when more needs to be
arned before a solution can be reached.

en we find ourselves in any new situation, we react with
stress. As we discuss in the Emotions key, new and unusual experiences have the habit of activating our amygdala — the brain's
alarm bell.

If we have the necessary knowledge to solve the problem, or
if we can adapt our knowledge so as to avoid being frightened,
our primary strategy takes effect; it is the problem-solver. At the
same time, our positive emotions signal that we are on the right
track; solving this problem becomes associated with joy.

If, on the other hand, we do not arrive at a solution right away,
it is a signal to proceed with caution, to consider the situation one
more time, to take it easy, go for a walk, think differently, and
maybe search more before we take another shot at the problem.

Some people are quick to give up when faced with new challenges, some activate their stubbornness, while others become
curious. The point is that knowledge of your emotions is a prerequisite for adaptive learning. Without emotions, there is no
adaptive behaviour; without adaptive behaviour, there is no
learning.

However, stress can also take away your control and make
you ill — this is negative stress. According to the psychologist
Mihaly Csíkszentmihályi, you are in danger of negative stress
when the challenges you face surpass your abilities.

Negative stress is thus not a disease, but rather, a signal that
you should unwind. The first signs of negative stress are sleep
problems, indicating that an important energy generator is fail-
ing. You consolidate your memory during deep sleep, so one of
the symptoms of stress is forgetfulness. Eventually, the chain
snaps at its weakest link and illnesses appear.

Negative stress is a bodily reaction to a challenge that can have an inner or an outer cause. We can think our way to such stress, through worrying and sorrow. And we can be stressed from too much work, from all the things we do not have time to do. Some people stress more easily than others, and we are stressed differently at different points in the day. Some are stressed from baby-sitting, while others enjoy it — it all depends on our perception and framing (⇨ PERCEPTION).

While negative stress is an expression of over-exertion and a signal that one should have lowered the tempo long ago, positive stress is a necessary energy that promotes learning.

The trick is to keep an eye on the warning lights in the secondary strategy. If you do not succeed in applying either strategy, you will likely experience extreme stress, inhibiting your learning and shrinking the hippocampus, which is crucial to our memory.

Positive stress, on the other hand, promotes chemical processes in the brain that stimulate nerve-cell growth and increase the number of nerve cells in the areas involved with learning.[8] At the same time, mild stress increases the quantity of neurohormones, which improves the brain's plasticity and reorganisation.[9]

And while chronic stress blunts the memory, acute stress improves it.[10] If you go for a run shortly after work, you remember what you learned better than if you slouched on the couch. This is because the increased brain activity enhances the memory encoding process.

It is not so much the quantity of work we face which is stressful — it is the uncertainty that it causes. Worrying about what we might not have time for is a well-known signal of uncertainty, and the number of new factors and new initiatives challenge our ability to adapt. Stress factors are requirements for which there

is no immediate or automatic adaptive response.[11] It also deals with having too many goals, too many open-ended intentions, and an insufficient capacity or overview to sort through them, to approach them, and to achieve them. To prevent negative stress, therefore, we must start by increasing the feeling of certainty. This requires insight, skills (creativity is important here), and, not least, the necessary time.

Playing the Body key

There is lots for us to learn from the musical mindset in relation to the body. The body is the musician's first instrument, really: its expressive skills reflect the emotional sensitivity of the musician in relation to the musical elements.

Musicians, like other performers, know the sensation of "butterflies in the stomach." For a beginner, this may be interpreted as an indication that "This is not for me," or "I'm no good at this," "I can't do it," "I'd better give up." A Pyramid of Failure is building up — body, language, focus – nervousness pervades.

But the elite performer will then say, "Hey, wait a second — the butterflies are meant to be there." The positive stress helps you perform and releases the needed adrenaline.

Mindfulness is also a core aspect of outstanding performances. Musicians talk about having their attention "in" their fingers when they play. It is important to let go of any mechanical or technical preoccupations and enter the "flow" state where they are one with their instrument and the music. It is a unique presence that touches and inspires the people who listen.

Musicians build up their competencies by constantly working with and training their bodies' expressive skills. It takes approximately 10,000 hours of practice to excel at something.[12] The violinist, the pianist, the guitarist have all "been there, done that."

They have integrated the music into every muscle fibre of their being. They *are* the music when they play.

Likewise, adopting a musical mindset means knowing that your experiences and practice are stored in your body. You can access and re-activate former successes and resources through your body, through the Pyramid of Success (⇨ SUCCESSES). Whatever you do, when you are at your very best, and "peak-performing," you are in the flow, fully immersed in a feeling of energy, focus, and involvement.

A musical mindset includes knowing that your experiences are stored in your body.

By learning to notice your body's signals — and exploring the effects of introducing small changes (⇨ GOALS) — you can create a relationship where your body is a core messenger that you will want to listen to and adjust. It will let you know when you are on track and when you are off-track. It offers the kind of feedback that is absolutely vital to take into account when embarking on a journey of change.

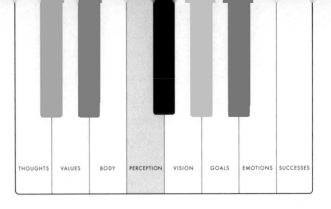

THOUGHTS | VALUES | BODY | PERCEPTION | VISION | GOALS | EMOTIONS | SUCCESSES

4

Perception

≡

Directing your interpretations

OUR INTERPRETATIONS of things are like lenses we wear: they decide how we label situations and name things. They are, however, rather arbitrary, and could easily be quite different. It very much boils down to what we look for and what we notice. For musicians, for all of us, perception essentially determines how we feel and how we perform. Do we consider something a potential threat? Or do we see the fun, challenging, enabling aspects? Musicality is very much about "tasting" the effects of interpretations — and deliberately changing them when needed, often tens of times a day. This builds another core aspect of the musical mind: resilience, the ability to bounce back to resourcefulness when challenged emotionally.

What story do you want to tell?

You have most likely heard expressions like these before:

- The glass is half-empty.
- The glass is half-full.
- We do not see the world as it is, but as we are.

They imply that what you see is determined by what you *choose* to see — every minute of your life. It boils down to your perception of things and your ability to decide where you focus your attention.

Two concepts that will help you appreciate this better are "framing" and "reframing."[1] Framing is about how we attend to and interpret the situations we are faced with. Reframing refers to changing our perception by focusing on other objects and explanations and thus interpreting a situation in different ways.[2]

Framing is about how we interpret situations.

The concept of framing is used, for example, within the world of photography. A photographer chooses his "frame" when he decides how to shoot his subject. Should he choose a frog's-eye view or a bird's-eye view? Does he want to be on eye level with the subject? Should he take a close-up or a long shot? Should he focus on one person, on another, or on several people at once? Determining the most effective angle assumes that the photographer knows what effect he wants to create. What story does he want to tell? What is his goal? And which values will he thereby honour (⇨GOALS, VALUES)?

Framing is also used in the world of music. A musician chooses his "frame" when he decides how to approach a piece of music. Should he choose the whole piece, or a smaller part? One way is to play the entire piece several times. Another is to concentrate only on each part. And a third strategy is to combine the

whole and the part approach. It is essential to have a repertoire of strategies as a musician, and the knowledge of strategies is referred to as "metacognitive knowledge." It is knowledge of how different strategies may satisfy different tasks and goals – and how to oscillate between framing and reframing when the interplay between part and whole is set in action. Knowing a piece of music is different from knowing a list of facts; it is a process of getting to know a living creation, approaching it from different angles. This enables you to get ever-new experiences from listening to the same piece of music at various times.

There is no such thing as one true framing.

Likewise for you: the framing you choose in any given situation is crucial to its effect — emotionally, mentally, behaviourally, and physically. To illustrate this, let us consider an example:

Your telephone has not rung for a week. If you choose to frame your situation as "I am lonely," then you will very likely feel sad, maybe even frustrated and angry. If you call someone with that frame of mind and in that condition, you may end up sounding offended that they have not called you. Perhaps they will be puzzled by your tone. Perhaps this will lead to discord?

Now, reframe the situation. For example, you could choose to explore which values you want to have stimulated: "Who would I prefer to talk to right now? What does this person represent that is important to me? What could my next step be?"

Or, you could look for cracks in the "truth" of your initial framing — here your loneliness: "It may be true that no-one has called for a week. On the other hand, I met my friend for a cup of coffee over the weekend, and I have two messages from good friends in my inbox."

Or, you also have the choice of looking at the positive side of being on your own for a while, a so-called "benefit-finding process": "Perhaps I feel a bit isolated right now. On the other hand, this has enabled me to meet my deadline at work, and I was able to finish reading that great novel."

Take note of the effects these three reframings have on you. One of them probably works better for you than the others. None of them contains the "absolute truth" about your situation. However, neither did the original framing!

When we talk about framing and reframing there is no such thing as a "true" one. There are useful framings, and less useful ones. Useful framings lead to resourcefulness; less useful framings drain your resourcefulness. So practise reframing and exercising your choice actively:

① Feel the effects of your current framing.
② Consider if these effects are useful for you; do they lead you in a direction you want to go in?
③ Approach a number of potential reframings in a playful way.
④ Choose a reframing that makes you resourceful.
⑤ Implant this reframing into your brain and mindset.
⑥ Feel the effects on your emotions, your thoughts, your actions, and your body.

The more accustomed you get to playing your inner piano, the smoother and easier this process becomes. But, if this is a new area for you, you should expect to have to train this change of perception many times — maybe for several months — before it becomes natural to you.

What you expect is what you see

Musicians know better than anyone that what you expect is what you see. If you are playing a concert and you consider it an

ordeal of being scrutinised by your audience, those furrows on the foreheads of some people in the audience are what you will notice. If you perceive that you are where you are as a consequence of some odd mistake — "They're going to find out in a minute that I'm nothing special"— then every yawn is interpreted as proof of this. Talk about the brain becoming an opponent!

We are biased towards confirming our existing beliefs.

We filter all our experiences according to our initial perceptions. Our perception of reality is so dependent upon our expectations, which in turn are based on our mental models and beliefs of the world. The American scientist Peter Senge puts it this way:

> *[We use] our established mental models to both define the problem and come up with the solutions. When we listen, we usually hear very little other than what we have heard before. "There she goes again," calls out in our heads. From that point onward, we selectively hear only what we recognise, interpret what we hear based on our past views and feelings, and draw conclusions much like those we have drawn before.*[3]

This selectivity is also called "confirmation bias"— we are biased towards confirming our existing beliefs.

Your choice of frame is linked to action; you apply your perception in life. Two women had similar work functions — canvassing and conducting sales meetings — but very different framings of their respective jobs. One of them experienced the meetings with her potential customers as "exams," which naturally caused inner resistance and made her feel uncomfortable. The other woman described her meetings as "conquests."

These are two very different perceptions of very similar,

recurring events. Which perception you choose will have major implications for how you use your energy before, during and after the meetings with your customers. Notice that what is important here is not how the meetings "actually" are. The world each of the women constructed was the basis for their interpretations and the world they acted upon.[4]

The point here is not that we should all start saying "conquest" when we feel we attend an "exam." The point is to increase awareness of your current framing, notice its effects, and creatively come up with a number of different frames you could choose to apply. What works well for one person may not be relevant at all for another person. The reframing you end up choosing has contagious effects on your actions and results – so if it does not deliver resourcefulness, choose another way of reframing.

How reframing works

Researchers know a great deal about framing and reframing. A study conducted by the psychologists Ethan Kross and Ozlem Ayduk provides unique insight into the nature of reframing.[5]

The study participants were divided into three groups, and asked to recall unpleasant memories from their lives — and then to do one of the following:

- ◉ Focus on the feeling, and be associated[6] into the emotion, as in rumination[7] — *Feel!*
- ◉ Participate in or think about other things — *Distract yourself!*
- ◉ Review the experience as though watching it on a screen — *Dissociate!*

The researchers discovered that the emotional effect was significantly different depending on which strategy the subjects used:

Strategy	Emotional effect (anger, sadness)	
	Same day	*A week later*
Feel!	Worsened	Remained the same
Distract!	Reduced	Remained the same
Dissociate!	Reduced	Further reduced

The emotional effect of *Feel!* clearly demonstrated that the subjects became even more angry or sad and, a week later, the feelings surrounding the situation were the same. Things had not improved; the anger and the sadness were still there.

The emotional effect of *Distract!* and *Dissociate!* caused the subjects to feel less angry or sad for the moment, but the effects after a week varied. The people who had distracted themselves through actions or thoughts were still vulnerable to the situation one week later. Allowing oneself to be distracted does not transform the meaning of the experience, and presumably does not change the interpretation of similar situations in the future, hence the continued vulnerability towards the situation. The explanation for this is simple. It is called Hebb's Law, which states (as poetically formulated by the Irish professor Ian Robertson): "Cells that fire together, wire together."[8] When two strategies — in this case the thought of something unpleasant combined with thinking of something else — interact with each other, the content is maintained. This way, a framing takes place that, in this case, one would call a consolidation of the emotional memory.[9]

By contrast, with people who dissociated — in other words who consciously reviewed the event like a movie, from a different and more distant angle — the emotional effect was further reduced after a week. Dissociation is not the same as forgetting. You change track, and thereby change your explanation of the situation — and hence change your emotions too. By means of dissociation, you stretch your perspective, and create a new memory, which is remembered positively.[10]

When the alarm bell of the brain starts ringing

When you play the Perception key, bear in mind that your perceptions directly influence the activity in your amygdala, the brain's alarm bell.

When something is perceived as a danger or a threat, the amygdala says, "Stop!" and this message is transmitted throughout the body. This is a thoroughly good thing when it protects us. When we walked the ancient forests, the amygdala's coding was crucial to our survival. But today, the amygdala fires not only in situations perceived as physical dangers, but also in "dangerous" situations of more symbolic character: exams, meetings, public speaking, new habits, organisational changes, etc.

Amygdala activations, whether in face of physical or symbolic dangers, are accompanied by bodily tension, quicker pulse, draining of oxygen and sugar from the blood, release of cortisol (the "stress hormone") from the adrenal gland, and typically also by catastrophic thoughts regarding the danger level of the situation (⇨ BODY, THOUGHTS).

Research has shown that when you see a "neutral" image and interpret it negatively, the amygdala activity in the brain increases. If you then move to interpreting it more neutrally or positively, amygdala activity decreases. Therefore, if you are in the habit of interpreting situations negatively, you will activate the amygdala far more often than if you are in the habit of interpreting situations neutrally or positively.

Today, brain researchers know that all emotions are present at all times.[11] They are found below the surface, like seeds ready to sprout. One or two may dominate your consciousness right now, but you have potential access to all emotions all the time. To a large degree, this is what enables reframing: you can choose to "pick" another flower — i.e., another emotion — than the one that dominates right now. As if you were walking through a meadow in spring, you choose which flowers to pick.

All emotions are present at all times, ready to sprout.

This is why at, say, a funeral, some of the guests may be in deep mourning for their loss, while others feel joy about a life well-lived, and the way the deceased touched their own lives. Or you may have attended a wedding where the groom cried tears of joy from start to finish, while the bride just beamed with happiness. These behaviours take place as interplays of the Perception, Thoughts, Emotions, and Body keys.

Robinson Crusoe reframing

First and foremost, the world as we experience it is brought to life in our minds. The situation *itself*, as it exists "in reality," affects our emotions to a far lesser degree.

Sonja Lyubomirsky, a leading expert on positive psychology, asserts that genetics determine a starting point (a "set point") for our happiness. It makes up 50 per cent of our "happiness score." Ten per cent is dependent on our life's objective circumstances and experiences. And most important, 40 per cent of the perceived happiness is attributed to what we can directly influence, not least through our perception.[12]

This says a great deal about the extent to which we can influence our satisfaction and happiness in life. It also says a great deal about how little significance the failed relationship, the layoffs at work or that illness actually have for our perceived happiness.

Even for people who are certain that a change of president in their country will make them happier, research shows that after their dream turns into reality, they end up being exactly as happy or unhappy, optimistic or pessimistic as they were before.[13]

Two brothers find themselves in very different life situations; one has become a successful businessman with a good family, whereas the other is lonely, unemployed, and severely addicted to alcohol. Both make use of the same explanation: "My father was an alcoholic." Now, what is the truth in this case? The truth is... subjective. The same actual circumstance — their father being an alcoholic — made one of them a fighter and the other a victim. The narratives we construct and choose to maintain about our own lives are crucial to how resourceful we think ourselves to be, and to the development we undergo.

You can choose to direct your attention to the positive side of things, as in the "Robinson Crusoe" reframing method[14] below:

Minus	Plus
− I am on a deserted island without hope of rescue.	+ But I am alive and I did not drown like everyone else on the ship.
− I am isolated from the whole world, and sentenced to a miserable life.	+ But I was also separated from everyone else on board and thus avoided death.
− I have no clothes to wear.	+ But I am in a warm climate where I would hardly want to wear clothes even if I had any.

The American National Institute of Mental Health tested this method (from the world of cognitive behavioural therapy[15]) on several hundred participants, all suffering from moderate-severe to severe depression. Sixty per cent were cured of their severe depression using only exercises similar to this.

Now, we do not claim that changing your perceptions can cure psychological problems just like that. In many cases, therapeutic counselling is necessary. We only want to emphasise how effective activities like these are for seeing the bright side of things, and for finding opportunities rather than limitations.

The maps that help you navigate

Each day we live, we create internal representations of the outside world in our minds. These "maps" help us filter our experiences and navigate the world. Maps develop over time, fed with whatever you give attention to.[16] The teenager who spends his evenings watching internet porn will grow different brain maps from the teenager playing squash or the one reading classics. Your maps are created by your experiences, your expectations, your defeats and your victories, your fears, your beliefs, and your culture. Combined, these maps "colour" what you experience and what you choose. Your current perceived reality is thus the sum of what you have paid attention to so far in life.

Your colleagues, boss, spouse, and acquaintances have their own maps. If you share an experience — such as a concert, an argument, a speech, or a jog — they may well assess it and conclude very differently than you. Basically, people witnessing the same situation are highly unlikely to have had the same experience, because they pay attention to different things, based on their unique maps.

Our maps represent "the truth" for us. If we hear something

that does not fit our maps, we are more likely to reject it than to change our maps. If we hear something that is inspirational to us, but it still does not match our maps, we may try to implement it — but we will most likely fail.

A music teacher might tell a student what it feels like to be in the "zone," but it may not land. She might say to the student, "I try to get into the feeling of being in love. I create butterflies in my stomach." But if the student has never been deeply in love — or if "love" has lots of negative connotations for him — it may not be his way of entering his zone. It may be that his way of creating a super-useful state is by imagining himself travelling, feeling the buzz of things and the excitement before flying. However, for a person who is a frequent flyer, it may take yet another focus to create those butterflies in the stomach and the right level of excitement. A good teacher knows this, and will encourage the student to explore what works for him or her.

If a certain framing does not make you resourceful, it is a good idea to change your circumstances, change your framing, or both. But if you hear a framing you would really like to implement, and yet it does not "strike home," then it is an indication that you may be better off trying out another one. Or if, say, you decide to try a new framing or do something, but nothing then "happens," it may well be because there was a misalignment between your decision and your internal maps. It is all a matter of tailoring your piano-playing style to your own internal maps, and those of the people you interact with. So

If a framing doesn't strike home, you may be better off trying another one.

before you start blaming yourself for being "lazy," or start losing faith in your ability to change, first change your framing strategy. And if that doesn't seem to deliver either, change it again.

Plasticity makes change possible

Brain researchers know that our brains undergo concrete changes as a consequence of where we focus our attention. Our maps are plastic; they evolve over time. Some people's maps evolve rather slowly and fairly little; others' evolve considerably faster and to a greater degree.[17] Your brain's plasticity makes it crucial that you notice what you are focusing on, because wherever you have your attention — whether it is on your needs, football, amusing events, a good habit, nervousness, sex, or shoes — you are channelling energy into that subject. And whatever you give energy to, grows.

You may be familiar with being kept awake by a dripping tap, or an alarm clock that ticks too loudly. The more you listen, the louder it gets. Naturally, your perception is playing a trick on you, since no one is turning up the volume. But, because you start paying attention to the sound, and choose to perceive it as annoying, your level of irritation goes up until it becomes unbearable and you jump out of bed to make it stop. Even though it may seem impossible to you under those circumstances, some people actually do not mind those sounds. And yet other people are capable of attending to the sound, only to let go of the sound. The difference is found not in the "truth" about a dripping tap or a ticking clock, but in your framings.

Many people choose to say, "I cannot tolerate x." In this way, they put an equal sign between themselves (their identity) and intolerance to a certain noise, a certain behaviour, or other similar things. However, no matter how impossible it may seem, reframing is actually possible. It is possible to go from not being able to tolerate that ticking clock to thinking it is just fine — and it is possible to go from being afraid of public speaking to thinking that it is exciting and motivating.

The American neuroscientist Jeffrey M. Schwartz puts it this way: "Wherever we direct our brain's attention, this is where we create and strengthen the brain's connections. If we direct our attention towards negative things, then it is these connections that are created and strengthened."[18] If we direct our attention and inner dialogue to the ticking clock and the belief that we cannot tolerate it — it will grow bigger and wind us up (⇨THOUGHTS).

Your volatile framings

Your brain's susceptibility to influence is great — far greater than you may think[19]:

In an experiment that demonstrates the so-called "focusing illusion," a group of students was asked to answer two questions, in the specified order:

① "How happy are you with your life in general?"

and then,

② "How many dates have you been on in the last month?"

When asked the questions in this order, there was no significant connection between happiness and dates.

Then, the question order was changed:

① "How many dates have you been on in the last month?"

and then,

② "How happy are you with your life in general?"

When questioned this way, the students perceived happiness as linked to romance — and now, all of a sudden, something that would not have otherwise been relevant to their happiness became a factor: the more dates, the happier the person.

This small change to the formulation of the questions changed the landscape that the participants used to create meaning. And this is a general pattern. The subject that comes first sets the framework for the following one. It changes your attention and

thus also your assessment; you answer differently.

Did you know that you can actually stress people by asking them about stress? If you ask a group of employees: "On a scale of 1 to 10, how stressed are you?" the attention points towards the word "stress." People begin to consider how stressed they are — and they suddenly notice stress, even though they may never have thought of themselves as being stressed. Suddenly the whole department is "struck by stress"— and there we go again.

Optimists vs. pessimists

Language has the magical ability to direct attention. That is a common thread in this book. Where do you direct your attention? How do you use language? Often it only takes a twist of your perception, and completely different emotions and thoughts take off from there.

One of the things worth noticing is whether your patterns are generally optimistic or pessimistic. Pessimists interpret their setbacks and frustrations by assuming that the cause is something permanent, pervasive, and personal. For example: "It will never get better." "It will undermine everything." "It's my fault." The psychologist Martin Seligman has found that pessimists are eight times more susceptible to depression when something goes wrong in their lives, and they perform worse in school, at sports, and on the job market.[20]

Meanwhile, optimists interpret setbacks and frustrations as something surmountable, particular to a single problem, and resulting from temporary circumstances or other people[21]: "It did not go quite as planned this time. But next time I can start afresh, and I will do X instead."

Ever wondered what your perception patterns have been like until now? What does it sound like when you play your

Perception key? If you were a musician, would you be happy with the timbre or would you adjust your instrument?

Your current perceptions can be changed, and the first important step is to notice them, discover them. Even though the "old" pattern is not washed away like letters written on a sandy beach, in time you will become very familiar with the optimistic alternative and be able to use it actively in your daily life. If

Your perceptions can be changed; the first step is to notice them.

you find yourself repeating an old pattern — which is perfectly normal — and then start blaming yourself or giving up — like many people do — you will not change. But if you notice, reformulate and then walk down the more optimistic path, change is not only eminently possible but, over time, highly likely.

Tramp a new path in the forest

Many people think that they are creating something new in their lives by suppressing old habits. But our brains do not work this way. You cannot actively do away with and delete networks in your brain. And by talking about them and analysing them to bits you risk reinforcing the very brain networks you want less activation of, hence making matters worse.

So, if you want more of the same then by all means focus on it. But if you want less of it, then what you have to do instead is to *tramp a new path in the forest* — and go down that new path as often as possible.

On the stretch where the new path is tramped, the old one falls into disuse and fades into the background. It is inhibited, but it can be brought back, since paths that have once been tramped never fully disappear.

A newborn baby is born with primitive reflexes, which

"disappear" with age because they are inhibited. But, if an adult damages his cerebral cortex, this inhibition can fall away, and the primitive reflexes may show again. This shows that the reflexes only appear to have disappeared.

Hebb's Law tells us that "neurons that fire together, wire together"; "neurons that fire apart, wire apart."[22] This is important knowledge when you tramp a new path in the forest. Each time you tramp the new path, you strengthen the relevant nerve connections of this new habit. And the nerve connections relevant to the old habit become weaker and weaker until they appear to have disappeared.

Neurons that fire together, wire together.

That does not mean that you cannot experience a set-back and find yourself repeating the old behaviour. But it means that even when this happens, you may just gracefully return to the new one, strengthening the relevant nerve connections as you do so.

Trip-wires along the way

It is not always easy to tramp new paths as you may find trip-wires scattered about. Some of the trip-wires that inhibit personal development and genuine change include worry, self-criticism, and the habit of seeing things from a fixed, rigid perspective (⇨THOUGHTS, SUCCESSES).

However, it is also a bad habit to look for unambiguous answers to ambiguous questions. "Why do I do this again and again?" "I wonder why I feel like this?" "Why did things turned out in such a horrible way?" "What did I do to deserve this?" These are all different variations of questions that lead your attention in the same direction: down the path you do not want to go down — in other words, focusing more attention on the "bad" habit. You shine the "torch" of your brain—i.e., your attention—in the hope of finding an answer—a single cause to a complexly built habit. However, what would you benefit from finding that answer? How sure are you that there is only one answer? And how sure are you that the answer you find is the most meaningful and useful one? Often people come up with "one true answer" that does not necessarily serve them. It may create a gap between you and your loved ones and thus conflict with some important values of yours (⇨ VALUES).

There are many dead-ends on your path to genuine change. One of them is becoming manically obsessed with your "Why?" This does not mean that you should not be interested in motives, reasons, and patterns, but it does mean that you should learn to shift your curiosity towards what you want to create, towards the vision that you want to realise, and towards the direction that you want to go in (⇨ VISION, GOALS).

Seeing the positives of "doggy bags"

Professor Jack Mezirow defines three forms of reflection: content reflection, process reflection, and premise reflection.[23] Only the last — premise reflection — has the power to transform your perspective, and to create a reframing of your perception of a situation or problem. Through this form of reflection, you question your assumptions, beliefs, and values, and you become more aware of what these mean to the way you view the world.

You can do this in many ways. One of the most effective methods is to look at things through different lenses than the ones you are currently using.

One such exercise traces the *positive* side-effects of bad habits:

⦿ First, identify something that you consider a bad habit, e.g., mismanaging your time, or often arriving late.

- Then, ask yourself: What does this habit actually give me? What else do I get from it? What positive side-effects stem from this habit?"

You do this until you have a list of benefits. If you are persistent and open to your own answers — even the surprising ones — you can end up with a long list of items. 20? 30? 50? What this exercise does is force you to consciously challenge your framing of the habit — from judging it as bad and stupid, to identifying its benefits. There are good reasons for us having habits — even the ones we currently consider bad — and changing our perspective is crucial to changing our behaviour and introducing new habits.

A man defined one of his bad habits as always cooking too much food when his children came to visit. After asking himself the kinds of questions above, he arrived at a long list of positive side-effects to this bad habit. For example, he held the values of "hospitality" and "generosity" in high regard. He gained an opportunity to "show care" for his children by preparing them doggy bags. He remembered his own childhood home, where food was scarce, and he realised that by cooking more than enough he actually set another standard — "abundance"— for his children to gain from. He felt that, in this way, he provided comfort. And love. The fact that there was so much food usually also led to joking and laughter, and this served as a way for him and the children to "bond." From perceiving this habit as something negative and worth fighting, he genuinely changed his take on it.

Another man considered his evening cigarette a bad habit. He would smoke it in the kitchen at night with his wife, after their kids had gone to bed. After going through this exercise, he better understood why he kept doing it. Every evening, he and his wife would go over the events of the day. He noted that they would "reflect" together and "share" with each other. He felt "close" to her. He felt "relaxed" and "balanced" (balance was a core value of his by the way). He would get an overview of the day that had just passed, and an outlook on the day that was soon to come. The cigarette in the kitchen marked the "transition to a special kind of intimacy," now that the children were asleep.

This simple exercise led to premise reflection for both the men. That which was initially framed as a problem and a bad habit changed its face. It ended with the first man not wanting to change the behaviour after all, because he had now come to see the habit in a different light entirely. The second man realised that some important needs were met through this habit — and that they should be met in *other* ways, if he was to be successful in quitting the cigarettes.

When a habit meets a number of important needs, to imagine that you can just erase it is an illusion. You are very likely to fall back into the old "bad" habit if you do not get to see the number of positive effects it has in your life, and the values this particular behaviour hon-

When a habit meets important needs, it is an illusion to imagine that you can just erase it.

ours (⇨ VALUES). But when you realise the positive effects, you can start being creative in coming up with new ways of meeting the identified needs.

Playing the Perception key

In essence, playing the Perception key is about creating premise reflection. It opens our eyes to the assumptions we have always taken for granted. When the premises change, so does the conclusion. Try it yourself!

To stretch your perspective of any given situation, look at it from multiple angles: not only as "you," but also as if you were

the other person(s) involved, or someone completely neutral. These perspectives are also called First, Second and Third position respectively.

When you step into another person's shoes and do your best to explore how he or she thinks and feels, you make a creative leap.

When you step into the shoes of a neutral observer, you see the particular situation as if from a distance, allowing you to notice the relational dynamics, shared intentions and values, and possible solutions too. It is a bit like watching a movie: you see yourself, the people you interact with and the unfolding situation. Researchers know that stepping back and gaining perspective nurtures creative problem-solving.[24] You could say that such third-person awareness paves the way for intrapersonal and interpersonal innovation, allowing you to come up with genuinely new takes on situations and relationships.

All three positions are useful. Some people are very good at being in one of the positions but not so good at moving to the others. It is a muscle that can be trained, a flexibility that can be learned. The greatest degree of understanding — and the most wisdom — is derived from having the flexibility to move in and out of all three positions.

A musician who plays different pieces of music in succession will also go in and out of different composers' intentions and musical languages while playing. He also needs to be good at going in and out of the positions of the audience too: Who are they? What do they expect? Which adjustments will make a difference — and enable them to understand and treasure the "language" of the music?

The most wisdom is derived from having the flexibility to move in and out of all three positions.

The musician is not only playing for but with the audience, and the audience response can enhance the perception of a performance a great deal. In order to shift positions smoothly, the musician must have a flexible, open mindset — and that is in fact at the core of the supreme musician.

Audience response is important to your performance not least because of the so-called "Rosenthal effect"[25]: Other people's expectations are of great importance to your performance — they tend to become self-fulfilling prophecies. If they think little of you, this will show in their actions and expectations too; you will "shrink" and thus perform worse. If they think highly of you, this will show in their actions and expectations too; you will grow and blossom and perform better. Whether you spiral upwards or downwards in a given situation or environment, therefore, does not depend solely on you, but also on your surroundings, the people who form your audience, their perceptions and their "micro-messages" (⇨EMOTIONS).

The goal of reframing is an emotion — resourcefulness — which also manifests in a bodily experience. And as you test your number of different reframing options, playing the Perception key, you actually use the Vision, Values, Emotions and Body keys to imagine and sense what that reframing will be like. Notice here how interconnected the keys of your inner piano are.

Notice how interconnected the keys of your inner piano are.

When you play the Perception key, remember the famous saying, "All beginnings are difficult." Anything you do the first time, the second time, or rarely, will feel unusual, awkward — and these feelings can easily make us give up. The more you train, the more used you will become to the sound and the potential of the Perception key — and the more you will gain from

it. Whether you need to analyse, communicate, mediate, plan or create in your daily life, being skilled in stretching your own perspective is a major advantage.

In the longer run, you will probably find that you change framings fluently. It may then not be one, golden reframing you repeat all the time. You will instead have built up the ability to sense your current framing at any given moment, feel the effects, come up with alternatives, choose and apply the most suitable, notice the difference, and — if the perceptual difference was not substantial enough — do the process over again, until you achieve the most useful, most inspiring perspective.

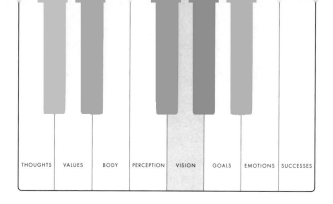

| THOUGHTS | VALUES | BODY | PERCEPTION | VISION | GOALS | EMOTIONS | SUCCESSES |

5

Vision

Rehearsing the future

BUILDING A PICTURE of one's future performance is a powerful skill. Each time you project this picture and mentally rehearse the situation as vividly as possible, the brain is prepared to go out and "do it" in a similar way. In fact, mental training can deliver results similar to practical training. It is therefore an immeasurably rewarding investment for you to build your visualisation skills, and — like a musician — oscillate smoothly between the intuitive, visual system of the brain and the analytical, verbal one. This chapter will go the first steps with you so that you may build a strong vision for yourself and turn it into reality.

We are moved by vision

What is vision? When you are in the presence of a true visionary,

you know it. His eyes shine brightly and decisively. His words move you. You are struck by a desire to be part of the vision, to be a co-creator of the future he paints.

"Where there is no vision, the people perish," is a quotation from the Old Testament. Try for a moment to reflect on the importance of vision for a people, for a nation, and for a culture.

We need visions, dreams, and images of the future that spark hope and action.

The most powerful leaders are those who nourish vision, who have a clear picture of where they — and we — are going. They are the ones who move us, with their integrity and their words, and awaken images inside us. Just as you are reading this, it is very likely that your visual system is working and you already see a powerful leader in your mind's eye.

The quotation says something else that is important: Where there is no vision, the people perish. Perish! We need visions, dreams, and images of the future that spark hope and action — or else we perish.

A vision is an idea or a conception of the future. Visionary thinking is based upon a particular form of thinking: imagination. The visionary's brain is therefore full of pictures. We can find the visionary in politics, but also in the worlds of business, science and art. Influential managers, eminent writers and successful entrepreneurs share one thing in common: they are visionaries. They can envision the future, anticipate events, and put the necessary strategies in motion so as to achieve the goals they set.[1]

You too have the ability to create inner images. Have you ever tried reading a book and then later felt disappointed while watching the movie version — because it did not fit the pictures you had created? Most people answer "yes" to this question. If you are one of them, it shows that you too can create images and visions, even though it may be a skill you have not yet consciously developed.

Your future-oriented memory

When we use our imaginations and engage in visual thinking, a significant part of this activity takes place in the frontal pole of the brain's frontal lobes.[2] Researchers have shown that you use the same area of the brain whether you are remembering something that has happened, or imagining that something will happen. They also know that to the brain, simulating an action is the same as performing it. Thus a very important link exists between your memories of the past, your visions of the future, and your ability to perform successfully in the present.

If your memory is untrained or full of holes, there are probably also holes in your ability to envision the future, your visualisation of what you want to happen. And vice versa. If you want to train your ability to visualise the future, then start by telling vivid stories of the past.

To put it a different way, it seems as though evolution has made memory future-oriented.[3] Researchers speak of "memory for the future,"[4] but this facility is not equally well-developed in all of us.

As we already know, memory is "filled up" with knowledge, but this knowledge can be seized by our imagination or narrative circuit (⇨THOUGHTS) and be directed towards new possibilities in the future.

But could the memory also, in a way, hold back the imagination? A group of researchers is now working on the hypothesis that if one is too good at remembering, and one knows too much, this inhibits the memory for the future. On the other hand,

people who are very forgetful find they need to compensate for their forgetfulness by reconstructing their memory with their imagination. When the Danish poet Piet Hein turned 80, he was asked what he thought he was particularly good at. He was not in doubt: "I am good at forgetting." Having expert knowledge is great, but so is forgetfulness, since you are then forced to start anew, to imagine, to create.

You can use this knowledge directly, in your daily life and when playing your inner piano. The brain's working memory has a very limited capacity. The more you try to remember, the fuller your working memory becomes, and the less room there is for new ideas and insights. Therefore, always make sure you have paper and pen with you — as your "external memory." Jot things down. Then you will remember them, and at the same time free up space in your working memory. But, you must also accept that you will forget a lot — and that is good!

Always have paper and pen with you — as your "external memory."

If you start fighting the fact that you will forget things (even lots of things), you tie a lot of energy to this. In fact, the belief that you are bad at remembering makes you forget even more. Training up the ability to trust your memory is a huge investment. It will come, when it comes! A thought or an idea — that fled before you paid enough attention to it — will come back if you trust it will and if there is "room" for it in your working memory. If, however, your working memory is packed with open intentions and pieces of information — and you don't apply the principle of using an external memory — it will be messy and chaotic in there, and leave no room for great thoughts to (re)visit.

So start experimenting. Try storing things in some form of external memory and see what works for you. Scribble on post-it notes, in a notebook, on your iPhone? Make an ever-evolving mind map? Make regular recordings of your thoughts and ideas? Which methods work for you — and to what degree they suit your lifestyle — can only be explored by one person!

Start telling vivid stories about your past too. And create pictures in your head of potential future scenarios. You can train your drive by having your vision in plain sight and, at the same time, being open to the outcome; things will never be exactly as you had expected them to be, so you must accept that and prepare yourself to manoeuvre flexibly.

In order to excel at playing on your inner piano, you must train up your ability to create images for your inner eye. And when you see the images before you — and they are brought to life in your mind — then you activate the same part of the brain as when you go out and do it.

Applying the relevant mental system: slow vs. fast

Two mental systems exist in the brain: a slow one and a fast one. Their interplay is very important when it comes to building your vision and getting insights that will move you towards your vision.

The idea of two mental systems in the brain is not new. In fact, this has been described since the ancient Greeks spoke of "Apollonian" and "Dionysian" sides; since Freud differentiated between the rational consciousness and spontaneity in our subconscious; and it is described too when one highlights the difference between analytical and intuitive thinking. Today, brain research has more to add.[5]

The two systems are actually complementary; this means that they operate in relation to each another, and can be turned up or down according to the particular situation, challenge or goal:

- The *slow system* is analytical, explicit, sequential, controlled, and has a low capacity.
- The *fast system* is holistic, implicit, parallel, automatic, and has a large capacity.

This difference can be positively exploited. Before you start working on a task, it is a good idea to evaluate whether it is simple or complex. If the task is simple, you are better off using the slow system and working analytically. If it is complex, you should use the fast one and listen to your intuition.

This may seem surprising, for we often do the exact opposite! If, say, an organisation has a complex problem, the slow systems are called upon and long meetings are held — which eventually arrive at the same result one expected from the beginning.

The Dutch researcher Ap Dijksterhuis sent a group of test subjects shopping in two different ways, at two different locations. They were supposed to shop either slowly, reflecting on their choices, or quickly and spontaneously. First, they were asked to buy an article of clothing — a simple task. The results showed that the slow shoppers were far more satisfied with their purchases than the fast shoppers. The test subjects were then asked to furnish an apartment with furniture from a shop. In this case, it was the fast shoppers who were more satisfied.[6] Simple decisions benefit the most from rational, conscious thought, while complicated decisions are best made using emotions and intuition.

If the task is simple, use your slow system; if the task is hard, use your fast one.

In another study, Dijksterhuis asked several groups of participants to select the best car out of four options. One group was given four factors on which to make their selections. For this group, the slow, analytic approach worked best: more than half the time, the test subjects chose the best of the four cars using this approach. Another group was intentionally distracted during their analytical processing, and then forced to make a fast decision. They performed significantly worse. However, when the complexity of the experiment increased something interesting happened. Now, the test subjects were supposed to make their decision based on 12 factors — a far more complex, and likely, scenario. In this case, the analytical strategy was successful less than 25 per cent of the time. The best-performing group for this complex decision, as it turned out, was given the facts about the cars, and then interrupted and made to do a crossword puzzle. Then, they were asked to return to the cars and make a quick decision. Forced to utilise a more feeling-oriented decision-making process, they found the best car 60 per cent of the time.[7]

What is the explanation for this? It is very simple. When you have to solve a complex problem, such as furnishing an apartment or being an entrepreneur, it requires such a large brain capacity that the slow thinking system cannot handle it. On the other hand, the fast system has the large capacity that is necessary, and, at the same time, it is able to draw upon empirical knowledge from the slow system. Therefore, you should follow your gut feeling in complex situations — but remember that you can make mistakes, particularly when strong emotions are involved.

What does this mean for playing your inner piano? A lot indeed, because, if you believe that you have to analyse your way to answers to the complex challenges in your life, you are mistaken. It would be beneficial for you to train the interaction between the fast and the slow systems, to feel and listen to the intuition of the fast system and to move the idea then to the slow system and scrutinise it with your analytical abilities. Or vice versa. Start analysing the situation, and then release the tension

of concentration by inviting the body to play along—take a walk, do some exercise, sleep on it—and allow the insights (which are very visual) to arrive.

Refining your senses

The brain's slow system thinks in language, while the fast system thinks in images. You must get in touch with the fast system when you play the Vision key. We are different from other animals in our imagination and our reasoning; but, to assume that our development is based on rationality (i.e., "thinking with your head") is a misunderstanding.

Our point of departure, as human beings, is "bodily thinking." We think about both nature and society with our bodies, and imagine nature as a body — Mother Earth — which we impregnate in the spring when we sow our seeds in her naked soil.

This anthropomorphism (the attribution of human qualities to our environment) is fundamental to our rational and abstract intelligence. Our linguistic descriptions of things and of events are often founded in images of a body: the needle has an eye, a stool has legs, a comb has teeth, a bottle has a neck.

We are born with a body, with senses, and with a brain, before we even have language. The world we are born into is first and foremost a qualitative world of movement, colours, sounds, light, scents, and texture. A warm arm feels different from a rolling pin. Wood feels different from a carpet. Something is firm and something is soft; something is liquid and hot; something else is hard and cold. All this we can observe. But not only that. Already, at this sensory level, mental processes are at work, asking questions.

Things do not happen in sequence, with sensing first, then

perception, and finally cognition — "I feel, I perceive, I think."[8] In fact, the last two can affect and *control* your senses. The same touch can tickle one person unpleasantly and give pleasure to another. It is not about sensing as such, but rather about the filters that we apply to our senses: Have we decided to be ticklish or not? Is the touch pleasant, and is it from a person who has "permission" to tickle us?

The body with its senses and the mind with its mental processes are not two entities, but one. And becoming conscious of your surroundings therefore assumes a well-developed sensory apparatus. You can train yourself to recognise the qualities of the world you live in; put simply, learn to feel, to see, and to hear. In this way, the refinement of your senses becomes a crucial part of your development.

When you turn your "Observer" on — i.e., your ability to neutrally observe things (⇨THOUGHTS) — you gain access to a rich variety of sensory stimuli. The senses hold information that can be ever so useful in your current situation. This increases your chances of coming up with more useful interpretations of a situation than the ones you may stick to when your sensory openness is more restricted.

Perception and cognition can affect and control your senses.

Starting to pay more attention to the concrete experience of sensing and feeling in all situations is a sure way to strengthen your ability to imagine. You may feel slightly vulnerable at first, but you will get more used to being highly receptive to the uniqueness of each situation. The learning from this slips straight into your episodic memory, which is your personal, picture-based memory.[9]

The episodic memory is the source of the images of your

imagination, and the narrative core of your identity. If your episodic memory is damaged, you lose both the ability to imagine and your personality. Therefore, your dynamic personality is closely connected with what has not yet occurred, and with your imagination of what could happen.

As you turn your senses on and start to experience things more vividly, you are likely to notice that they are connected to your emotions (⇨EMOTIONS). Your most powerful memories are likely to be experiences where your senses were laser-sharp. You need emotions to create a rich picture and a lasting memory. The same principle applies to storytelling. Storytelling arranges events in an emotionally meaningful pattern.

Here we reach a very important conclusion: Vision is an emotional pattern, because our imagination of the future is always connected to feelings — of excitement, curiosity, uncertainty, and fearfulness.

The Vision key does not "just" deal with the future. It also deals with the present. Your present. Your identity. Your core. Your values. You create your own reality through your vision. Which envisioned images do you nourish? And of the many possible outcomes that your choices might have, which do you see happening? Which emotional patterns do you currently experience when you imagine your future?

The dream behind the problem

We are culturally disposed to search for and focus on problems. Just check out the news — or a political debate — and count the number of problems covered and discussed. Problems are a core focus in the technical world, where, say, a machine is malfunctioning and has to be fixed. But development and human life as such do not have to have that focus.

"Behind every problem lies a frustrated dream," Peter Lang once said. You always have the choice of focusing on the "problem" or the underlying "dream." The former is often an example of playing the Thoughts key in a less constructive way; creating lots of problem-oriented inner dialogue that sets you on the downward spiral. The latter

You always have the choice of focusing on the problem or the underlying dream.

is an example of playing the Vision key, moving on to playing the Goals key, and the Emotions key. Problems make you feel stuck; dreams get you going.

To shed light on the difference between the two approaches, try this exercise. Choose a problem (or a "challenge") that you face in your life. It could be about time pressure, work-life balance, things you did not get done, a difficult relationship, etc.

First, examine the challenge with "problem lenses" on. Ask yourself:

- What is my problem? Give a specific instance of it.
- For how long have I had it?
- What are my worst experiences with the problem?
- How does the problem affect me?
- Why have I not solved the problem yet?

Feel the inner effect of these questions. How do they affect you? How do they affect your energy? How does your body feel?

Next, look at the challenge with "dream lenses" on and ask yourself:

- What is my dream? What does it look like and feel like?
- What will be the value of reaching this dream — for me, my family, my organisation?
- Which specific goal(s) will help me move closer, however slightly, to that dream?

- Which of my internal or external resources can help?
- In similar situations, what have I had success doing?
- What were my keys to success then?
- So, which exact steps will I take today in order to reach my goal and move closer to my dream?

Then feel the inner effect. How do these questions affect you? How do they affect your energy? How does your body feel?

You have now tried both the problem lenses and the dream lenses. What difference did you experience in their inner effect? We are dealing with a small shift in focus — but hopefully a large change of the inner effect.

When you leave your problem lenses behind, you also leave behind a very counterproductive strategy within the Thoughts domain: the pointing of the torch of your brain towards what you do not want more of.

Notice how the Vision, Values, Goals, and Successes keys take to the stage when you put your dream lenses on. It is a completely different way of approaching life — and you will feel the effect in your Body, Emotions, Perception and Thoughts key too.

Getting to know and play your inner piano, you will learn to recognise what problem lenses feel like and what it feels like to turn on your Vision.

Powerful entry points for insights

If you are overly concentrated — and in too much of a "problem-solving mode" — you will not reach an insight. You will be stuck in a mental impasse instead. Your good intentions thus become counterproductive because they are not in line with brain logic.

Researchers know that insight is preceded by a period of reflection. So, what is useful is to learn to "space out" a little! Look at things as if you are daydreaming, or as if you are trying to unfocus your eyes so as to make one of those 3-D "Magic Eye" pictures come alive. Experiment too with creating mental pictures — seeing things with your inner eye — adding colour, contour, clarity.

In the Successes chapter we further touch on what happens before an insight comes. But for now, know that the slow, analytical, verbal system in the brain is put to rest when you reflect by playing the Visions key. This paves the way for the fast, intuitive, visionary system — the superhero of insights. The insight comes and the whole body is ready for action. It is a very powerful thing to get to know this process by heart and thus make the most of your brain capacity.

In essence, you can view the eight keys of your inner piano as different entry points for the kind of relaxed reflection that will move you from your mental impasse to insight and action: Play the Perception key, and consider various potential reframings of the situation. Play the Successes key, and mentally browse your catalogue of successful experiences, full of unharvested learning. Play this Vision key, and space out visually, relaxing your face and forehead, maybe tilting your head slightly, looking thoughtful rather than concentrated.

In other words, when you feel stuck in your Thoughts key, learn to change keys. By knowing your inner piano, you will always have alternatives — new ways to go, and myriad options that can bring you closer to the change you want. In time this will prove to be a most worthwhile investment.

Dream questions to get you started

We are born, we live, we die. It is a journey with many milestones, but only the last one is certain. Have you ever tried to make an imaginary journey to the very end of your life and then

look back? What sort of life would you want to look back on? What did you contribute? What difference have you made? Is anything missing?

Make that imaginary journey now, and while you are there — before you travel back to the present — take an inner snapshot of the vision you see before you. Ask yourself: What makes this thoroughly meaningful? Which specific goals would help to turn this vision into reality?

A vision can thus be connected to your life's big agenda, to the bigger difference that you want to make through your life. But, it can also be connected to a smaller agenda, to a conversation, a task or an event you are facing.

Remember that a vision is an image. To get you started creating your vision, you may want to begin with some so-called "dream questions":

- If I were a multimillionaire and did not have to worry about my income, I would…
- If I could solve one world problem right now, it would be…
- I would most like to work for free for…
- The greatest, most mind-blowing thing I can see myself doing is…
- If I were a head of state, I would first make sure that…
- If I were certain to succeed, I would dare to…
- If I could shape the future, I would…
- The footprints I would most like to leave in this world are…
- If I were guaranteed success, I would…
- What I would most like to influence people with is…

If you have a vision but it is not very clear, then add colour, contour, and detail. Take note of how you feel. How might your image be modified so that you turn up the good feelings? Which values do you honour through your vision? Who is with you in this picture? Which goals are you achieving? What makes the vision important?

When you first see the vision and take a mental snapshot of it, you can start deciphering it, understanding its elements by putting them into words and analysing them in detail. This is another example of the interplay between the fast, visual system of the brain, and the slow, analytical one.

Your imagination is the key to your future because your mental concept of how things could be will enable you to see them. Your mental images con-trol your senses and your per-ception, because you always see and perceive something based on your experiences and the images generated by your imagination. You do not see reality; you shape it yourself.

You do not merely *see* reality; you shape it yourself.

Therefore, luck is not something one has; it is something one creates. You put yourself in places where luck is likely to happen. And visualising makes the likelihood of winning much greater.

How "mind sculpture" helps you grow

Let us now look at a powerful way of using your vision called "mind sculpture,"[11] which shows how *mental* training can enhance *physical* training.

If we start in the world of music, we know that each finger has its own corresponding area in the cerebral cortex, and this area grows when the pianist practises every day. Practice makes perfect. If researchers scan the pianist's brain, they can see that the area of the brain dedicated to the hands is larger here than in most other people.

But let us suppose for a minute that the pianist trains his fingers using his imagination only. He studies the notes and imagines himself playing. This is what the pianist Glenn Gould did before he entered the recording studio[12] and it was particularly effective. Physical exercises can increase the strength of the fingers by 30 per cent, in relation to a control group that does not perform the same exercises. However, if you train mentally with the same fingers, their strength is increased by 22 per cent — and that's without lifting a finger. Our imagination trains our nerve cells.[13]

Our imagination trains our nerve cells! This is powerful stuff. It highlights the importance of mental readiness and rehearsal. Studies show that people who focus on directing fresh blood to their big toes actually increase the blood circulation in the area.[14] The same is true for many areas of your life and career: what you focus patiently and intently on boosting will be boosted.

> **What you focus patiently and intently on will be boosted.**

You can learn to perform mind sculpture, and bring your future vision to life using all your senses. To do so, you must be *associated* into the experience, meaning intensely present. See what you see; hear what you hear; feel what you feel; smell what you smell; and taste what you taste — as if you were there!

When the javelin athlete Steve Backley injured his ankle four weeks prior to the start of the competition season, he was unable to engage in any physical training. Instead, he made mind sculptures,[15] throwing thousands of "mental javelins." After two weeks of this type of training, he could resume his physical training at almost the same level as before his injury.

A prerequisite of mind sculptures is that your brain is already trained. You thus generate a kind of repetition of skills. If you have never thrown a javelin, you would probably not be very good at imagining it; it would only help a little.

This is precisely the reason the Successes key is so important: you must learn to get into touch with your successful experiences, even the ones you have forgotten.

Yes, you may not have delivered a speech in front of 300 people before, but you have probably given a presentation to 10 people, or talked with passion with two other people. Recall those events and your resourcefulness there, practise entering this particular state (⇨ BODY), and slowly build a picture of you applying this power to the future situation, here the speech before an audience of 300.

Thus mind sculpture becomes possible by accessing the many fragments of experience you have "in store." Remember even a world champion was a beginner once. Keep your faith! It will come. You will grow your abilities as you engage in mind sculpturing.

When people code and store their experiences, there are certain structural similarities:

- Either you look back upon the experience through your own eyes and see what you saw back then — you are *associated*;

- Or you see yourself physically in the experience, as though you were watching everything on a screen — you are *dissociated*.

Sometimes it is extremely useful to add some distance between you and a situation: it helps regulate emotions and promote creative problem-solving[16] (⇨ PERCEPTION). But right now, when the goal is to bring your vision to life, it is important to associate yourself fully into the experience. Use all your senses. It is not enough to see your past experiences before you, as though you

were watching yourself on film. Instead, you must specifically imagine yourself doing it, as if you were doing it! This mental preparation makes the brain feel on "homeground" when you later find yourself in the situation.

You now have a good basis for bringing your vision to life — and parts of you are already on the hunt for the physical experience of what you have just created mentally.

Your imagination is not exclusively about sight. You can form images with all your senses. You can probably visualise a freshly baked loaf of bread, but can you also imagine the smell, or the taste of the crisp crust? Can you think of a melody and play it in your mind? Can you imagine the sensation of wet, green grass beneath your feet? The more senses you activate, the richer your imagination grows. You are on the track to "mind sculpturing" now.

Out-of-this-world imagination

When you recall something, you recreate what you previously sensed and experienced. Your imagination consists of both recalling and creating new images.

The process of recalling is a very good example at how subjective our filters are — and how perception colours it all. The very same experience may be stored and recalled completely different by two people. One may think that his assignment was not good enough because the boss passed three critical remarks. But the boss may think that three critical remarks is very few and that it shows the report was in fact very good work. As these two people each recall the same situation, their imaginations add creatively to the memory, pulling them further apart. That is why you can come across two people fighting over memories, over what "actually" happened. They are both convinced that their personal interpretation is the real one and that the other is in the wrong. Human beings can waste an awful amount of time thus trying to fight each other's unique mental maps.

The ability to remember and imagine is an important part of our cognition, but also of our culture, because an important pre-requisite of a dynamic culture is the ability to imagine what the world could be.

It is quite amusing to look at pictures from 50 years ago, of what people then thought the world would look like today. Their imagination was rooted in how the world was 50 years ago — and it was extrapolated based on that logic. For example, computers, mobile phones, and espresso machines as we know them today do not feature in those images. They could not be imagined.

Remember this when you create pictures of your own future. The images — your vision — will undoubtedly have their point of origin in your life right now — and be limited by your current beliefs about what is true and possible. This is why miracle questions are such an important part of the play on your inner piano: "What if I could..." "What if, say, time was not a limitation — what would I then do for others?"

Your vision is limited by your current beliefs about what is true and possible.

"What if x and y were not opposites — what action would I then take?" Notice how vision interacts with perception and beliefs.

Even when you break the framework of your vision, it still has its roots in what is known today. This shows us the challenge of radical visualisation. It is not easy to think completely out of the box. But some people can, for instance in the worlds of art or science. Some composers, authors, and scientists are capable of creating scenarios and theories that are "out of this world" and where only history will prove their ingenuity and relevance.

Therefore, you may want to start building your visionary skills by looking at things from a "helicopter perspective" (⇨PERCEPTION). You may even want to take a look from a "rocket perspective" — looking down at things from really, really far away, from where you can see patterns and interconnections that were hitherto hidden.

Another powerful way of strengthening your vision is to play with different scenarios without judging them (⇨THOUGHTS). Be observant as you imagine different futures. Be open to many meaningful opportunities — not just one right solution. This fixation on the "right answer" dominates our culture, but is often inconsistent with everyday situations and challenges, because human life can rarely be healthily managed by an "either/or" distinction. There is almost always more than one solution. Most problems call for several clever, meaningful solutions rather than one true answer.

> **Most problems call for several clever solutions, not one "true" answer.**

And when you are faced with this wealth of options, and you find they all appeal to you to some extent, it is because they each have value to you (⇨VALUES). Instead of fighting it, start exploring what value dwells in each of the options.

And who says it has to be an either/or choice? What if the best parts of all the choices could be combined into one solution? And if not all the options can be realised, what can you learn from the things that could not be realised? (These could be values that you might want to nourish in a different way or at a different time.)

If you feel stuck in an either/or conundrum for a longer period of time, you may actually want to let go of both, in order to move your attention to a third or fourth option. One of the many tricky things about either/or choices is that they become interlinked in your brain as a result of Hebb's Law — "Neurons that fire together, wire together." Even when you choose the one and not the other, whenever you walk down the path you have chosen, you are likely to be reminded often (and maybe painfully) of the opportunity you left behind.

Playing the Vision key

When you play the Vision key, you direct your attention towards what you want to realise in life. Once you have touched upon your vision, it can be reality-tested, and then adjusted and made operational through meaningful goals and actions.

Playing the Vision key also shifts your reflection into gear, prompting you to ask yourself:

- If I wrote a book about the essence of my leadership, what would the title be?
- If I had a magic wand and could fulfil any wish, what would it be?
- What kind of world would I like to create?
- Ten years from now, when I look back on this period of my life, what would be the main thing I learned?
- If I had to tell a story about a person that was in a similar situation, how would it go?

All these Vision questions stimulate your image-creation, your values and your passion.

Coaching and self-coaching have much in common with positive psychology,[17] in that your attention is consciously directed "away from pathology and suffering" and "towards strength, vision, and dreams,"[18] as the psychologist Carol Kauffmann writes.

The Vision key is closely interconnected with the other keys. When you visualise successfully, you experience inner silence

— no inner chattering, just clear focus. In this way you can affect the Thoughts key (including your inner dialogue) and the Emotions key by playing your Vision key.

In order to strengthen that clear focus and inner silence, you may want to play your Body key and explore the power of the closed eyes. It is no wonder that musicians — when they play at their best — often have their eyes closed.

When in the "zone," there is inner silence. It shuts out some of the stimuli not needed in the given situation and it enhances their connection to the music and visualisation of the extraordinary piece of music. This inner silence is also experienced by other elite performers. When they are in their "zone" there is inner silence. When they are less resourceful, there is inner noise and self-doubt.

When you find yourself thinking about a problem you have, ask yourself what the dream behind it is. Make that dream — the vision — bigger by giving attention to it and applying the visual techniques of this key.

Our "problems"— as well as our problem-oriented inner dialogue (⇨THOUGHTS) — are often created by a less-useful framing (⇨PERCEPTION), by a dismaying feeling of some of our values being disrespected (⇨VALUES, EMOTIONS), by a misdirected focus on what went wrong instead of what works (⇨SUCCESSES), by a lack of vision of where we want to go (⇨VISION), and by a lack of concrete measures to vivify that vision (⇨GOALS). And not to forget, our body language often traps us in a problem's mode (⇨BODY). Again it is obvious that the keys of your inner piano are closely interlinked — and if you feel stuck playing one or two, simply play some of the others and see where that takes you.

Playing your Vision key successfully is thus very much down to experimentation, trust and incremental competency development, that is, having the courage to try out, explore, be creative and playful, be less successful (maybe) and yet not judging but staying curious — and continuing to trust that you will grow your ability to see an attractive future and move towards it, step by step.

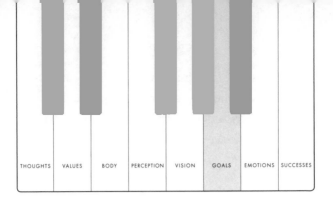

| THOUGHTS | VALUES | BODY | PERCEPTION | VISION | GOALS | EMOTIONS | SUCCESSES |

6

Goals

≡

Making your dreams attainable

MUSICIANS KNOW that consistent practice is necessary to excel. It requires the ability to set and pursue goals, both long-term goals (what it takes to reach the bigger dream) and short-term ones (what is needed now in order to develop one's play). Juggling different goals — while having a good time doing it — will help you make your aspirations attainable. This chapter will help you understand how to formulate and pursue goals in the most flexible, engaging and efficient way.

Goals and vision are two different things. Vision is an *image* — of what you want to create and achieve. Goals are the *actions* that will help you to realise it. Some people have an easy time forming visions, but a harder time defining which goals must be met to realise this vision — they are "dreamers," and currently lack a sense of operationalisation. Others think a lot in terms of goals and only a little in terms of vision — they are "doers," but they lack perspective and direction. Where are you on this scale?

Actually, many people define goal after goal, without having a clear picture of the vision and the deeper meaning behind it all, that is, the values honoured by the scenario they aim for (⇨ VALUES). This is one of the reasons why goals, vision and values each have their own chapter in this book — because even though, in an ideal world, they work together very closely, they each have their own individual justification.

Make goals your point of departure

If you have previously been involved with coaching, you know that goals are important. The GROW model, which is one of the most well-known coaching models in the world,[1] offers four phases of coaching: Goal, Realities, Options, and Will.

It is not a coincidence that the goal formulation is the very first phase. This is largely because it sets the direction and plots the course. It is also because, during a thorough goal-formulation process, many issues change their appearance, fall into place, and solve themselves. A reframing takes place (⇨ PERCEPTION) — and the issues that troubled you cease to be issues altogether.

The saying that "a goal properly set is halfway reached" highlights the importance of this phase. Many people are inclined to first talk about a situation, and *then* formulate the goal. However, John Whitmore, the founder of GROW, says that a goal based on existing reality tends to become either negative (say, a reaction to a problem and limited by our thinking), or to generate the opposite effect of what is intended. Short-sighted solutions can lead us astray from long-term goals.[2]

The most effective goals are formulated in the present tense,

as if you are "already there." Instead of saying, "I need to become better at saying 'No,'" you should express your goal like this: "I know my priorities and communicate them succinctly and respectfully." Or, "I know when and where to set my limits." When you formulate your goals in such a way, and say them out loud, you immediately put yourself on track to making it happen — because the brain does not know the difference between simulation and action (⇨VISION).

Learning from Wonderland

To make changes in your life (and to "tramp a new path" in the brain, ⇨PERCEPTION) presumes that you have some idea where you want to go. If not, you are like Alice in Wonderland:

> — *Cheshire Puss... Would you tell me, please, which way*
> *I ought to go from here?*
> — *That depends a good deal on where you want to get to,*
> *said the Cat.*
> — *I don't much care where, said Alice.*
> — *Then it doesn't matter which way you go, said the Cat.*[3]

When you know where you want to go you have a so-called "towards" goal.[4] By contrast, you can also have "away from" goals — which are formulated as something you want to avoid, unlearn and get away from. Like Alice.

Let us look at another example, Bob. He says, "I want to get rid of my administrative tasks"— which is an "away from" goal. He knows that he wants less of this in his life. But, where does he want to go? Does he want to delegate his administrative tasks to a co-worker? Hire someone to take care of them? Train his competencies so he can perform the tasks faster? Or does Bob want to switch to a different job altogether — and if so, what job? Just because we know what we don't want, it doesn't necessarily mean we have a clue where to go next.

It is not unusual to be set in motion by an "away from" goal. There may be some sort of a "burning platform," and you need to take immediate and maybe even radical steps. But, having started out that way, if you know how to play your inner piano, you will begin to supplement it with a "towards" goal. If you want to continue moving, you will benefit from knowing the direction. For this, you need to build up your visualisation skills (⇨ VISION).

If, however, like many people, you only know your "away from" goal — and if you fool yourself into believing that this is *the* goal — you end up expending your energy on it, and in fact strengthen the brain connections in this area. The more you attempt to run away from such a goal, the more fixedly you will be tied to it. "I don't want to be nervous, I don't want to be nervous, I don't want to be nervous" — and slowly the nervousness takes control, even in the farthest corners of the body.

The word "don't" is a symbolic formulation. But the brain's fast system, which deals with the "Don't" sentence, is *not* a symbolic one; it is a literal one. It thinks in specific images, and cannot operate with a negation. It notices the focus of the thought — say nervousness — but *not* whether we want what is in focus. Therefore the brain removes the word "don't," and our subconscious process hears, "I want to be nervous" — which makes you even more nervous.

> **The fast system notices the focus (e.g., nervousness), but not whether we want it!**

How then do you turn this "away from" goal into a "towards" goal? Instead of saying, "I don't want to be nervous," try to articulate an alternative, say, "I am breathing calmly, in, out, in, out."

Notice that the goal is formulated in the present tense, thereby drawing the perception process into the picture. The sentence "I am breathing calmly" becomes a self-fulfilling prophecy; you turn your breathing into your co-player, because what you focus on, expands and eventualises.

The psychologists Coats, Janoff-Bulman and Alpert have found that people who are inclined to set "away from" goals have a greater tendency towards depression. Other studies — for example by Elliot, Sheldon, and Church — confirm that pursuing "away from" goals over longer periods of time is associated with diminished well-being, while "towards" goals lead to greater well-being and better performance.[5]

> **"Towards" goals lead to greater well-being and better performance.**

In recent years, brain research has discovered how effective it is to programme the brain with what you want to achieve. When you imagine a "towards" goal, you simultaneously initiate a readiness to undertake the actions necessary to achieve it. To the brain, simulating an action is the same as carrying it out.[6] What happens is a kind of mental rehearsal — one that makes it all the more likely that what you desire will happen (⇨ VISION).

So, practise creating images and perceptions of what you want more of in life. Be very specific. You must also split your journey up into manageable parts, as we will show you below.

Dreams on legs

Goals are couplings of vision and action — dreams on legs. It's all too easy to dream in blurry images of what one wants in the future. Many people set goals that send them on journeys, but along the way, they often forget what goals they set, and neglect to celebrate them or reward themselves when they achieve the goals. Some get used to the goal en route, others start turning their attention to new goals and don't recognise it when they reach the original goals, while others formulate their goals in such a vague way that they simply cannot determine when they reach it.

A teenage boy might dream of becoming a rock star. But what does it mean to be a rock star? When has he reached his goal? Is it when he sings on stage? Is it when there are at least 1000 people in the audience? Or when there are 40,000? Should the audience be satisfied, happy, or thrilled? How many stars should the critics give his concert? Or is he a rock star when he has released a CD? Two CDs? Ten?

If you set vague goals, you risk becoming restless and dissatisfied. Define clear goals, however, and you will be able to continuously compare them against reality ("How far am I?"), celebrate your successes, and adjust your plan for reaching them if you or your circumstances have changed along the way.

Make your goals specific, with definite time frames — and write them down. The psychologist Peter M. Gollwitzer performed an experiment that shows how important this is. At a university lecture — the last one before Christmas — he asked his students to send him a Christmas card no later than 48 hours after Christmas Eve. At this point, half the students were allowed to leave, while the remaining half were asked to operationalise their promise: When would they send the letter? And where would they send it from? Eventually, of the first group, one-third of the students sent cards to Gollwitzer; of the second group, two-thirds did so. Thus did Gollwitzer shine light on such "implementation intentions," which bridge the intention and the environment it needs to succeed.[7]

Now it is your turn to try. Write down a goal that is important

to you. Then, go through the Goal Checklist on the right, asking yourself whether your goal satisfies each of the ten conditions. Be critical but constructive in relation to your own formulation. As you go along, reformulate your goal. Tick the boxes when you feel sure that the criteria are met.

If you cannot wholeheartedly answer "Yes" to all the questions, stop and do something about it. Only when you have ticked "Yes" in all ten boxes are you ready to reformulate your goal — and to put this new formulation down on paper. It has to be extremely precise and comprehensible, and it must challenge you on whatever level you would like to be challenged.

Out of the box with flexible goal-focus

A musician needs strong goal-oriented behaviour. Excellence takes at least 10,000 hours of practice, as well as a strong sense of direction, a willingness to put other things aside for the higher aim, and the ability to cope with distractions and temptations along the way.

Goal-oriented behaviour has two different goals: *impersonal goals*, such as getting the garden ready for spring or fixing a puncture; and *socially oriented goals*, which deal with how you perceive yourself and others. There are manuals for impersonal goals, to teach you how to achieve them, but not for socially oriented goals — these we learn as we go along.

Switching between these two types of goals can, however, be valuable. If you have had an important breakthrough in the way you handle a difficult situation (a socially oriented goal), then try to decode what it was you actually did that worked. Imagine you are writing the manual for your successful experience (⇨ SUCCESSES) in the same way that one can have a manual for an impersonal goal. Now, move back, adopting the position of

126

Goal Checklist: Is your goal...

- A "towards" goal?
  If not, reformulate the goal as something you want to attain not get away from.   YES   NO

- A performance goal?
  If not, check you have full influence over your ability to achieve this goal.   YES   NO

- Specific?
  If not, reformulate the goal precisely and in detail.   YES   NO

- Measurable?
  If not, define a specific outcome that indicates your goal has been reached.   YES   NO

- Ambitious?
  If not, make sure the goal "stretches" you and challenges you enough.   YES   NO

- Realistic?
  If not, check that the goal is compatible with your situation/time/resources.   YES   NO

- Time-framed?
  If not, define a specific end-date for reaching this goal.   YES   NO

- Holistic?
  If not, make sure the goal is accepted by the people close to you, and fits your life.   YES   NO

- Attractive?
  If not, check whether the goal is worth striving for — also bearing costs in mind.   YES   NO

- Yours?
  If not, make sure you take full responsibility; you are the one to reach this goal.   YES   NO

someone who is in the process of learning. If you had an apprentice, what would he or she need to know to be able to follow in your footsteps and become successful in this too? Try out those elements again. See how they work. Imagine applying this to a future situation. Adjust the manual when needed. Test it again. Then practise your ability to act, and adjust flexibly, while you are in an actual situation with other people.

The brain's two frontal lobes — the right and the left — make up a good third of the cerebrum. With connections to pretty much all areas of the brain, they are the brain's headquarters, where coordination takes place. The frontmost part — the prefrontal cortex — plans the actions, which the rearmost motor region then puts into action. The prefrontal cortex consists of three areas: the lateral, which faces the ear; the medial, which is located on the inner side, such that the two medial areas of the frontal lobes meet at the medial line; and the frontal pole, found right up against the forehead. These three areas work closely together, with the following distribution of labour:

The brain's two frontal lobes are its "headquarters."

- *Lateral* — planning, problem-solving in the working memory, and goal-oriented behaviour in cooperation with the hippocampus.
- *Medial* — flexibility and emotional coordination in conjunction with the amygdala.
- *Frontal* — predicting the future.

Now imagine that you have to solve two problems — an easy one and a hard one. The first is relatively easy and you quickly find a solution. Now we increase the difficulty level. It may well become hard, if you continue to use the exact same strategy that you used to solve the easy problem.

Psychologists call this a "functional fixation," and it is typical of the lateral part of the prefrontal cortex. This section of the brain is quick to draw strategies from the long-term memory, (which it pulls into its working memory), but poor at changing strategies. It is good at thinking within the box, but not out of the box — to do that, the brain relies instead on the medial part. This is apparent in patients with a damaged lateral part but medial part intact: they have a hard time solving easy problems but not difficult ones.[8]

This interplay of your brain will be strengthened when you start to play your inner piano, to think outside the box, go inside it, only to get out of the box once again. In other words, be flexible and adaptable, and make relevant adjustments to your behaviour in relation to a challenge. Train yourself to find your successes, to learn from them — and to use your learning, adapted according to the requirements of each unique situation.

For example, when you find yourself in a situation where you are afraid, and the amygdala is inhibiting the medial part of your frontal lobes, you will be inclined to copy "known" strategies from the lateral part, whether they are truly useful for you or not. By doing so, you risk trying to solve the situation with the strategies that created it in the first place. Albert Einstein warned against believing that problems can be solved with the same strategies that created them. The art, therefore, is to find the peace of mind that can awaken the medial part, with its flexibility and greater ability to seek out new avenues.

When you are afraid, you copy "known" strategies, whether they are useful or not.

It is a matter of striking a fine balance. In the chapter on Successes, we suggest you make the most of your past achievements

and actively apply the learning from these. This will boost your sense of resourcefulness and inner motivation. However, the content of old strategies may not be relevant when it comes to new challenges. And if the goal is in fact product innovation, or the creation of something new, you may want to deliberately look elsewhere, other than to the content of your old strategies, to avoid a functional fixation.

Inner and outer motivation

Motivation is the driving force that can either promote or inhibit an action. It is a conscious or subconscious orientation towards or away from something.[9]

We are motivated to act when we receive *objective* criticism from others; this is a positive external driving force for creativity and innovation, and is perceived as a reward. We are inhibited from acting when we receive *subjective* criticism — a negative external motivator that is perceived as punishment.

When we are praised in moderation, we become inspired and "think up"; when we are punished, we feel put down and "think down." The body adapts correspondingly. Thinking up, we lift our heads, look about, and become happier. Our energy increases. We smile, and the blood supply to the brain increases; we straighten our backs, and our lungs receive more oxygen. We see opportunities rather than limitations. But when we think down, things grind to a halt. And if we become depressed, we sink very low indeed — till we can barely get out of bed in the morning.

When we "think up," we lift our heads, look about, and become happier.

People have different motivational patterns. Some have made themselves very dependent on outer motivation (also known as controlled motivation or external reference). Other people listen more to their own inner experience (also called autonomous motivation or internal reference).

Do you activate your drive when others say so, in the last possible moment, or when you want to impress others? Or is your personal drive derived from your desire (because you "just can't help it"), and from your inner wisdom? This is the difference between outer and inner motivation (⇨ SUCCESSES).

Outer motivation is found in the brain's slow system. Inner motivation belongs to the brain's fast system (⇨ VISION). Each has its own purpose, but when the goal is creativity and innovation, as it is in many organisations today, then internal motivation is the one to emphasise.[10] A powerful way of nurturing this is to ensure a strong interplay

Inner motivation can be strengthened through a deeper knowledge of your values.

between values, vision, insights, processes and results, allowing for highly self-regulated employees to be at their best, pursue their passions, and deliver extraordinary results.

With proper consideration, nurturing inner motivation does not preclude the use of external motivation. But some of us become dependent on praise, other people's opinions, and external motivation — and this kind of dependency kills inner motivation, because it removes our initiative and our personal vision.

If we connect this to goal-formulation and celebration, then clear goals enable celebration, while celebration enables reward, and reward enables (more) action.

Inner motivation can be strengthened through a deeper knowledge of your own values, through an understanding of and belief in your own experiences, as well as through the training of the ability to use yourself flexibly. In this manner, playing your

inner piano strengthens your inner motivation.

Play your inner piano, and you nourish your insights. Brain research seems to suggest that insight is directly related to the reward system of the brain[12]: You experience pleasant rewards when you arrive at new insights — and this gives you inner motivation to continue.

Small steps towards your goal

Pursuing goals in a brain-based way requires you to apply the "small steps" method. "Even a journey of a thousand miles begins with one step," noted Lao Tzu, 2500 years ago.

It's all too easy to formulate pompous plans, flashy projects intended to induce change, and "I am going to do it now" New Year's resolutions. But they impede our progress because the bar is set too high.

You are better off getting the brain to play along with the change. Train yourself to make the first steps safe and manageable.

The psychologist Robert Maurer illustrates the small-steps method[13] as follows:

Big goal ⇨ *Anxiety* ⇨ *Access to the thinking brain is limited* ⇨ *Failure*

Small goal ⇨ *Anxiety avoided* ⇨ *Thinking brain activated* ⇨ *Success*

By taking small, manageable steps in your development process, you avoid waking up your amygdala. The goal will not seem like a threat anymore, but rather an experiment or a game, and it will influence you in a different way.

If you document the changes taking place, such as by using the Habit Tracker on the next page, you stand a good chance of maintaining your overview and your optimism during the change process.

In the table, write down three or four new good habits. (We have started you off with two examples.) For each new habit, write down your goal (what you are aiming at, e.g., 100%), as well as your success criterion (what you would be satisfied with, e.g., 80%). Specifying a success criterion is a clever way of dealing with the "Judger" mindset that might otherwise make its appearance; by pondering and deciding what you would be satisfied with, you approach the process in a more relaxed and playful way — with a Learner's mindset (⇨ VISION).

Tick off each day that you are successful in implementing the habit. When the month is up, sum everything up in the "Total" row, and then calculate your success in per cent relative to the total number of days. Compare this with the defined goal and the success criterion. And see that you have taken important steps towards change — very likely more than you would have done (and noticed!) if you had not written them down.

Notice, too, how your "Judger" is silenced by bringing perspective to the table: "Yes, I may not have reached my goal of 100% — but I did indeed eat 24 apples this month."

As you continue with the small steps, and your thinking brain begins to "play along," new nerve connections are created. At the same time, you are re-telling the story of yourself — with nuanced and constructive language — and this positively changes your perception of your identity and strengthens your belief that change is in fact possible.

Habit Tracker: *August*			
Desired habit:	*Eat an apple a day*	*Pose deepening questions to employees when they ask my advice*	*More new habits...*
Goal:	*100%*	*80%*	
Criterion for success:	*75%*	*50%*	
Day 1	✓		
2	✓		
3	✓		
4	✓	✓	
5		✓	
6		*Weekend*	
7	✓	*Weekend*	
8	✓	✓	
9	✓		
10			
11	✓	✓	
12	✓	✓	
13		*Weekend*	
14	✓	*Weekend*	
15	✓		
16	✓	✓	
17	✓	✓	
18	✓	✓	
19		✓	
20	✓	*Weekend*	
21	✓	*Weekend*	
22	✓	✓	
23	✓	✓	
24	✓		
25		✓	
26	✓	✓	
27	✓	*Weekend*	
28	✓	*Weekend*	
29	✓	✓	
30		✓	
31	✓	✓	
Total count	*24 (of 31)*	*16 (of 23)*	
Success rate:	*77%*	*70%*	

When you decide to achieve a clear goal, the left prefrontal area of the brain is activated; it is an area that is extremely important for your mood, and which makes you strive to reach the goal and to control any negative emotions.

The left prefrontal area makes you strive to reach the goal.

Patience and small steps are virtues for your personal development. The more you insist on getting everything right now — and "the faster the better" — the more vulnerable your learning becomes. Enthusiasm and a thirst for learning are good drivers. But to think that you can just absorb and absorb, and expect everything to work right away — that's a pipe dream.

There is an important difference between "crammed practice" (e.g., intensive studying before an exam) and "spaced practice" (exploring and studying the same subject regularly over a long period of time). While crammed practice provides better immediate, short-term learning, spaced practice allows for better retention and performance over the long-term.[14]

If you are to build yourself up effectively, bear this in mind. The musician won't "get it" merely by practising manically. When the goal is building new habits and a broader repertoire into your "muscles" you may as well take advantage of this knowledge regarding spaced practice: Start experimenting with curiosity and patience — and allow learning to build up gradually, for the sake of your long-term benefits.[15]

Impatience is a well-known feeling when seeking new learning. New knowledge and new tasks can create confusion until the penny drops, and some people become irritated, frustrated or fearful when this confusion hits them. This can block your openness or make you give up on the change project all together.

A good reframing here is: "Confusion is the step before

understanding," or "Confusion is a sign that learning is on its way." These reframings help you accept what is — even confusion and uncertainty — instead of fighting the process.

When goals blind you

Even though goal-definition and goal-qualification are important, a lot of the "self-development wave" of today is, in our opinion, so goal-oriented that we feel the need to raise a warning flag: Goals can make you go blind!

Goals can make you focus so rigidly and eagerly on something that you limit other important aspects. Goal awareness is healthy — but goal fanaticism is not.

You may have experienced being late and being in so much of a hurry while held up in traffic that you think, "I hope there isn't an accident — I won't have time to help." Stop right there! There may well be a conflict between your goal and your values here. There most certainly is a conflict between your goal and the societal values of the culture you live in.

In fact, a thought-provoking study shows how goals can trump values, even when the values are practically written in capital letters in your consciousness. In this study, a group of theology students were assigned the task of giving a presentation based on the New Testament's parable of the Good Samaritan.[16] The speech was to be held in a building in another part of the university and, because of a tight schedule, the students had to hurry over to the venue. They did not know that the researchers had placed an actor on the way there, who would play a man in need of help, lying on the ground, coughing and manifestly

> Even though the students were on their way to speak on the Good Samaritan, most ignored the suffering man.

suffering. Even though these students were on their way to give a speech on the Good Samaritan, most of them ignored the suffering man. One actually stepped over him because the man was in his way.[17]

Goals — particularly when combined with time pressure and perceived stress — can blind you so much that you forget your own values and the behaviours that would honour these values (⇨ VALUES).

Playing the Goals key

Goals are dreams on legs. This is a great expression as it shows us the value of the Goals key. It is the key that grounds you thoroughly to reality. Together with the Body key, you need this to get going, to act — not blindfolded, but with a clear purpose, vision, and aim in sight.

The Goals key forces you to be specific. It offers help to keep the big overview on your road to change. Notice your progression — write it down.

The Goals key plays well together with the Values key. Before a meeting, define a goal, and decide which values are to shine clearly from you, no matter what happens. That will affect your Emotions, your Body, and your Thoughts. You may want to use the Perception key to disturb, challenge, or provoke your initial goal of the meeting; whether you perceive a meeting as a fight or as a chance to align priorities will make a big difference to how you formulate its goal.

> **Learn from the musician to juggle long-term goals and short-term ones.**

You may learn from the musician to juggle both long-term goals (the 10,000 hours of practice) and short-term goals (practising four hours every day this week) and at the same time enjoy

the music you make as you go along. Playfulness and presence are essentials aspects of a musical mindset — and these joyful states, intertwined with the more structured, focused, and regimented states, will accelerate your progress.

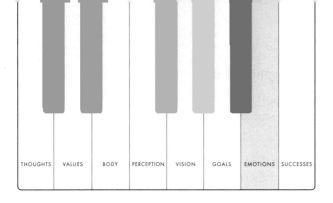

| THOUGHTS | VALUES | BODY | PERCEPTION | VISION | GOALS | EMOTIONS | SUCCESSES |

7

Emotions

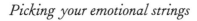

Picking your emotional strings

A MUSICIAN CAN choose to enter a particular emotion at full force. The most convincing performances are those where the emotional vibration is transmitted from the musician to the audience. All emotions are latently present inside of us all the time, and we — like musicians — must learn to decide which ones to give attention (and thus life) to at any given moment. Emotions can be increased or decreased in intensity by playing any of the other keys on your inner piano; hence they are *expressions of your current processes and habits* rather than *truthful witnesses of situations*. This chapter will show you how to feed your emotions in constructive ways and understand the vital role they play in your brain.

High-susceptibility alert

Your emotions are a great feedback mechanism. They let you know your state of mind and, if needed, invite you to change them. Emotions are programs of action. But unlike what many people think, emotions are not the "truth" about you or your situation — and there is not one "correct" interpretation, or perception, of a particular emotion.

Emotions are highly susceptible to being triggered by the other keys of your inner piano. If your Thought patterns are unconstructive, for example, you may act in ways that make you feel small. If a Goal seems too big, it triggers your amygdala, and sets off feelings of panic. If your Body is unenergetic, you feel down. If your framing of a situation is not useful, and your Perception thus works against your performance, you may be frightened to death. If you are not trained in building a Vision for yourself, you may be made anxious and fearful by thoughts of the future. If your Values are not respected, it may cause inner anger. And if you are not in the habit of noticing and revitalising your Successes, you may feel unaccomplished, depressed.

> Emotions are highly susceptible to being triggered by the other keys of your inner piano.

This is an incredibly important thing to remember. The next time you find yourself grappling with difficult emotions, try playing the other keys on your inner piano.

Most people do the exact opposite. When they are feeling sad, angry, insecure, they keep playing the Emotions key, intent on focusing on, talking about, and trying to diagnose "what is the matter." As an experiment, try instead to deliberately move your attention to one, two or three other keys and see where that takes you.

Watch out for emotional flu

Emotions may also have been transferred to you from other people. We human beings infect one another not just with colds and the flu, but also with emotions. People who interact regularly infect one another to a large degree. Colleagues, friends, and spouses are the most contagious for us. Harmful relationships can, therefore, work like a slow poison, whereas rewarding relationships have a positive effect on your health.

What would you like to be infected with? What would you not like to be infected with? Choose your social circle carefully! You are not just influenced by other people's emotions but also by their *reactions* to your emotions.[1]

Emotional infection takes place through a so-called "open loop" in our brains. When a system has an open loop, it relies on external sources to manage itself. By contrast, your body also contains closed-loop systems — e.g., your circulatory system, which regulates itself — meaning that what occurs in other people's circulatory systems does not affect yours. The open loop is also called the "mutual adaptation" between people.

The psychologist Daniel Goleman finds that we have an "inter-personal radar,"[2] and that the stronger our emotional connections to a person, the greater the mutual exchange; the most powerful exchanges take place between people who spend a lot of time together, day in, day out. For example, did you know that 50 to 70 per cent of the working climate of an office relates directly to the boss and his or her behaviour?[3] Thought-provoking, isn't it? But if you have ever been to a party where the hostess was angry or indifferent, you will know what we are talking about — the evening probably seemed like it was never going to end!

Your interaction with a person reshapes your brain's nerve pathways over the years. And you are not just being influenced

emotionally, but biologically too. In the workplace, women working closely together end up, over time, with similar menstruation cycles. A synchronisation of the interacting biological systems takes place. And it is not only hormone levels that are affected by our close surroundings — so too are heart functions, sleep rhythms, and immunity systems.

If you have the ability to steer your emotions in a positive direction and bring the best out in others, then you create "resonance."[4] That means you are in tune with yourself and the people around you. If, on the other hand, you steer your emotions in a negative direction, you spread "dissonance," or in other words, a disharmonic mood. So, one does not just speak of resonance and dissonance within music, but also in regards to human life.

In this area too, it is useful to be mindful[21] of the emotions you have right now, to know your values and your passion, and to explore what drives other people. Furthermore, it is about knowing where you want to go (⇨ VISION, GOALS, VALUES), as well as how you are going to get there (⇨ THOUGHTS, BODY, PERCEPTION, SUCCESSES).

Bear in mind that you also "infect" yourself emotionally all the time. Constructive habits can help you steer your emotions in constructive directions. If, for instance, you find yourself quick to anger, try to let an alternative grow instead — whether it is tranquility, acceptance, curiosity or something

Simply by focusing on being tranquil, you increase your tranquility.

else. Simply by focusing your attention on being tranquil, you increase your tranquility. How amazing is that! And this is down to the brain's logic: What you focus on, you get more of.

This has implications for the popular belief that "acting out" your negative emotions, e.g., anger, helps to purge them, and make you feel better. "Kick, shout, scream, or smack!" the idea goes; take it out on a pillow, hit it; give vent to your emotions, and you will be rid of them. But this technique is of little use, really, because when you focus on a particular emotion, you get more of it. The psychologist Brad Bushman showed in a study at Iowa State University that students who were asked to "act out" their anger felt far more aggressive afterwards than those who had been sitting in a quiet room for two minutes. The venting of anger does not extinguish the flame, as the psychologist Richard Wiseman puts it; instead, it pours oil on the fire.[6]

How body language influences emotions

In the Body key, we present the Pyramid of Success. It is a good example of how important body language is to your emotions. A little twist, a small change, and that can mean a huge difference in how you feel. Embodied-cognition research even suggests that the flexing of our facial muscles is necessary for our experiencing them. In other words, if we don't mimic happy emotions, we will not feel them.

Your body language includes how and how often you smile. There are two ways to smile: you can try to smile on purpose, or your emotional brain can make you smile. This is something a neurologist knows only too well, when he is seeing a patient who is paralysed on one side of the face. The patient cannot smile on command, but if he hears a joke, his face will light up in a big smile. How is this possible when the muscles of the face are inactive? The explanation is that the facial muscles are not paralysed; instead, the nerve connections, which are under the control of his will, cannot reach the muscles. The funny story, on the other hand, reaches his emotional brain directly, and *it* still has connections to the muscles.

Martin Seligman describes the difference between a "Duchenne smile" (a genuine smile) and a "Pan American smile" (a fake smile).[7] The Duchenne smile is characterised by the corners of the mouth moving upwards, and by the wrinkling of the skin at the corners of the eyes. The muscles responsible are called the obicularis oculi and the zygomaticus, and they are incredibly difficult to control by willpower. The Pan American smile has none of the Duchenne smile's characteristics, but instead resembles a cramp-induced grimace, like what lower primates display when they feel frightened.[8] A study from the University of California shows that students' yearbook smiles — are they genuine or fake? — can predict married-life and personal well-being for a 30-year period after college.

Students' yearbook smiles can predict their future well-being.

"Can a smile elect a president?" Brian Mullen asked himself, when he and his colleagues began to evaluate the body language of three television hosts at three networks during the presidential race between Ronald Reagan and Walter Mondale in 1984. They called viewers all over the country and asked whom they had voted for. Then, they studied the three television presenters. While two were neutral, the last one, Peter Jennings, was far more positive in his facial expressions and body language when he spoke of Reagan than of Mondale. The study showed that Jennings thereby influenced his viewers into voting for Reagan.[9]

If other people's body language can sell an opinion, could yours not do the same? Yes, it can! If researchers let test subjects assess the quality of various headsets, and then ask some of them to sit still, some to nod their heads (as though saying "yes") and some to shake their heads (as though saying "no"), what happens then? You have probably already guessed that the test subjects who nod their heads evaluate the headsets more positively than those who shake their heads.[10] This is another example of the "embodied cognition" introduced earlier (⇨BODY).

If we already have a positive or a negative take on something, our body language can play a part in amplifying these opinions. We nod when we express ourselves positively, and our body movements are rounded. We shake our heads when we speak of something negatively, and our body movements are more edgy. When others assess us based on our body language, calm and rounded movements are interpreted as those of a warm person, while abrupt and sharp movements are interpreted as cold.[11]

Changes in our facial musculature affect our state of mind because the muscles create an open circuit to the brain's emotional functions. If you smile while listening to a message, you will feel more positively about it than if you grimace. If you are prevented from smiling when happy, the intensity of the happy feeling

Changes in our facial musculature affect our state of mind.

is reduced.[12] The psychologist Robert Zajonc has even shown that it is enough to sing one vowel sound — and change your feelings.[13] Sing the "a" or "e" vowel 20 times and your mood improves; sing the "u" vowel and your mood deteriorates.

The brain's limbic system[14] has an indirect connection to the body's mimicry muscles. The emotions add timing, rhythm, and expression to the movements. One can move an arm more or less expressively, and these non-verbal signs can be more expressive than the verbal ones.

Previously, researchers thought, "I am happy, thus I smile." This is true for many people. Emotions easily reveal themselves from the inside out. But, today there is an important addition to that statement: "I smile, thus I become happy." Emotions can

actually be created — and be infectious — from the outside in. Your mimicry is such a powerful modulator of your emotions that you can use this activity to upgrade your happiness.

But do watch out when doing this! The idea is not just to "paste" a smile onto your face — that way you end up with a Pan American smile. Instead, consider your mimicry a tool for affecting your state; train it for set periods, in parallel with playing your inner piano.

Your constant emotional display

What happens when two people talk well together? They listen, move their arms and legs, turn their hands, fiddle with their clothes, and much more. But they do it in a special way: their movements are rhythmically coordinated. It is as though they are dancing together. They are on the same "wavelength." Even the tone and volume of their voices are synchronised, and these rhythms support verbal language and allow for extra nuances to be communicated between them.

William Condon, the pioneer within this area, calls these phenomena "cultural micro-rhythms," as they are culturally dependent and thus acquired. When two people have a good and fluent interaction with each other, it is also called "rapport," and people can have greater or lesser degrees of rapport in certain situations. Two people who are in rapport harmonise their energy levels, and copy one another, and this signals recognition and solidarity at a subconscious level.[15]

At this point, we would like to expand the concept of rapport. It is not just something you have with other people; it is also something that you have with yourself. All too often, people are their own worst critics and judges. And when they try to implement changes in their lives, they do so through orders and commands: "Pull yourself together!" (⇨THOUGHTS). They install a "coach from hell" in themselves. Do you do this too? Do you talk down to yourself — or do you talk respectfully to yourself? Do you enjoy your self-development journey or is it just something that you need to get over and done with? Do you constantly absorb learning and adapt your strategies, or do you insist on doing things in a certain way?

The rapport you develop with yourself and others has significant consequences for your emotions. How does it feel when you are on the same "wavelength" as someone else? What can another person say that is very motivating to you? Decode what is characteristic of these situations — and use the knowledge constructively by fine-tuning how you interact within yourself and with the world at large.

Several studies[16] have shown that you can predict the durability of a new marriage with great accuracy by observing how the couple talk to each other when they disagree. If the discussion is derogatory and does not accommodate both parties, or if one rolls his or her eyes while the other person is speaking, the prognosis is no good. If, on the other hand, they are open, communicate with respect, and listen well, it is an entirely different matter, a far more promising one.

Today we talk of "micro-messaging," the small, subtle messages — often subconscious — that pass between people without words.[17] Researchers from MIT found that we each send between 2000 and 4000 micro-messages a day, in the form of body language and intonation.

We each send between 2000 and 4000 micro-messages a day.

Let us consider a meeting scenario. One person is speaking, while the rest, ostensibly listening, send each other looks — looks

that say it all. They may not even be looking at the person who is speaking. Some of them may be looking at their watches or checking their mobiles. It may be that one or two move about in their seats. All of this is detected emotionally by the speaker — but it usually happens subconsciously and beyond language, and can therefore be very difficult to articulate and change.

If you have been on a communication course, you may have tried the exercise where a person is sent outside to prepare a small presentation for the group, while the rest of the group (the audience) agrees to show great interest in the presentation to begin with, only to switch at a predetermined point to displaying indifference. What happens in the room at that point? The energy flow that had been there during the early part of the presentation — the interplay between the speaker and the audience — becomes instantly impaired. The result is that the speaker is confused, uncertain, and put in doubt. So powerful are the micro-messages!

In that respect, authority as a speaker or trainer is not just something you acquire. It is a mandate given to you by your audience. Any experienced speaker will be able to tell you how different it is to walk into a room with an audience that attributes great emotions to your being there versus an audience who hardly knows who you are.

The world champion of reading micro-messages

Micro-messages are, to a large degree, the carriers of emotional infections, as they are picked up by the amygdala.

The amygdala is considered the warning mechanism of the brain. If something unexpected or threatening turns up, the amygdala reacts with fear, and the person withdraws, becoming passive or evasive.

The amygdala is a world champion at extracting emotional meaning from non-verbal messages, at the speed of light. These processes do not go through the verbal regions; they take place subconsciously. We then get sig- nals from the nerve pathways in our own body, which mimic the respective emotion experienced. That is how the infection takes place. The amygdala reads the emotional aspect of everything in our lives, subconsciously.

The amygdala reads the emotional aspect of everything in our lives, subconsciously.

When we look at, say, a photograph of a scared face, the amygdala reacts instantly. An fMRI-scan would show our brain patterns looking as though *we* are the ones being frightened, albeit on a less pronounced level.[18] The brain's mirror neurons are responsible in this case. They copy what they see in their surroundings.

Experiments with monkeys back in the 1990s (described in more detail in the Body key) showed that not only did the same area of the brain light up each time the monkey ate a banana, it also lit up when the monkey watched *another* monkey eat a banana. In other words, watching others perform an action activates the same brain region as when we do it ourselves. Thus when we see another person looking scared, we copy it reflexively.[19]

Today, brain researchers know that all emotions are latent at all times during a person's life. To a large degree, it is a prerequi- site of reframing (⇨PERCEPTION) that you can "pick" an emotion other than the one that is dominating right now. Being able to view your emotions externally or from above (as from a helicop- ter) helps you get a new perspective on them.

Hijacked in a sea of emotion

Do you recognise the experience of your inner alarm bell ringing? You body stiffens. Your heart races. Your thoughts run round in circles; they work you up. You get angry, or sad — and very much so. Psychologists say that people can be "hijacked," much like ships. Only this has to do with your emotions — and the pirate's name is amygdala.

The human brain is constructed so that any new challenge, opportunity or desire triggers a given level of anxiety. The amygdala is an alarm mechanism we share with all mammals; it controls our fight-or-flight response, and is hence crucial to our survival. Measurements show that the amygdala draws its conclusions much faster than the thinking brain. Neoconstructivist researchers — led by the psychologist Joseph LeDoux[20] — believe that this is because our brain contains two important circuits: a short circuit and a long one. The short circuit leads directly from the senses through a part of the interbrain called the thalamus to the amygdala. The long circuit leads through the cerebrum before reaching the amygdala, which takes more time. Hence, if you see something that is perceived as dangerous — a bear, for instance — the message travels to the amygdala via the short route. The amygdala declares "Danger!" and shuts down other needs, and the body is flooded with cortisol (the stress hormone) and adrenaline, which prepares it for action in an emergency situation. Specifically, brain functions unnecessary for the situation at hand are shut down (e.g., functions relating to digestion, sexual desire, intellectual thought processes). This makes perfect sense: Act now! — conscious understanding may come after.

There are a large number of connections between the thinking brain and the amygdala. But there are more connections *from* the amygdala to the thinking brain than vice versa, which means that the amygdala can flood and drown our conscious thinking by sending it a torrent of messages. An emotional reaction in the amygdala can arise before the thinking brain has had time to figure out what is going on.[21] This is convenient if we are face to face with a bear, but not at all convenient if the danger is of a symbolic

The amygdala does not recognise the difference between physical and symbolic dangers.

nature, e.g., delivering a speech, sitting for an examination, meeting new people, or exploring new behaviour patterns. The amygdala does not, however, recognise the difference between physical dangers and more symbolic dangers.[22]

How then do we go about building up the amydala's tolerance for the more symbolic dangers? For one, you could talk to yourself in a way that removes the drama and calms you down (⇨THOUGHTS). Or, you could reframe the situation from a "dangerous" one to, say, an "exciting" one. You could also grow your ability to feel when the amygdala is just about to be activated — and change focus (⇨PERCEPTION). You could also develop a useful breathing repertoire, and draw upon that to invoke inner calm (⇨BODY). Through playing your inner piano, you can get your amygdala to relax.

Each new challenge, desire, or opportunity, leads to a certain degree of cautiousness and, possibly, anxiety. Relative loss of status, certainty, autonomy, relatedness, and fairness can trigger the threat response too.[23] This awakening of the amygdala is perfectly normal, and it is something everyone experiences. People do differ, though, in how they interpret and act on such an experience:

◉ Some dramatise the anxiety and think there must be something wrong with them.

- Others conclude, "This just is not me." In other words, they put an equals sign between their identity and their behaviour, and refuse to try out behaviours that are different and new.

- Some feel the uncertainty but act anyway, maybe supported by some of the other keys on their inner piano, such as Perception (a calming reframing), Thought (empowering inner dialogue), Body (deep breathing), Vision (focusing on the bigger picture), Successes (recalling other times when success was achieved, in spite of "nerves").

- Some allow the feeling of anxiety or cautiousness to be the determining factor; they consistently choose the tasks and opportunities that trigger the amygdala — based on the logic that those are the ones that will benefit them the most.

Which of these do you do most of the time? And what effects does it have?

The storage of emotions at low resolution

The amygdala is responsible for our subconscious emotional learning. Imagine that you witnessed an accident where many people were involved. Some months later, you meet a person you do not recognise, but you instantly get a strong, unpleasant sensation. The amygdala has recognised the person as someone you met at the scene of the accident, and your brain now fires the same powerful emotions that you experienced in that situation. Or, you once ate some shrimp that made you ill, and ever since, you've had an aversion to the tiny creatures. You were criticised a lot as a child, and now as an adult, you react strongly when being criticised. You had a very unpleasant teacher at school who had a pointy nose, and now you cannot tolerate those kinds of noses. In all these cases, your mind made a connection between two aspects which would otherwise be unconnected. "Neurons that fire together, wire together," as Hebb's Law says[24] ($\Rightarrow$ PERCEPTION).

Unpleasant experiences can therefore hinder your development. They leave marks on the amygdala — both in terms of the emotions you've had and the choices you've made. This is why you may often find yourself making the same choices over and over again in critical situations. You ask your son to clear the table. He says, "In a minute." A few minutes after, you ask him to clear the table again. He repeats his earlier reply. And when he continues to lie on his bed — without having cleared the table — you feel that you are about to explode. That is the amygdala in action. You are caught in an emotion that you do not feel you can escape from or get rid of. It is as though a script has been written describing what will happen and what you will do, and you are just following it! Frustrating, isn't it?

What is crucial to know is that the amygdala stores emotional experiences at "low resolution." So even when a situation only mildly resembles an upsetting situation from the past, the amygdala recognises it as a similar situation — and the same emotions are triggered to deal with it. A branch in the forest looks like a snake. A piece of feedback from your boss seems as threatening as the time a former boss criticised you in front of your colleagues. A choice looks like a terrible dilemma, because you recall a decision-making process from the past that tore you apart.

Your magical fraction of a second

Brain researchers today know that there is a fraction of a second during which we can choose to stop a destructive emotional impulse.

The emotional impulses that occasionally explode within us draw nourishment from the so-called "schemas." A schema is a mental model of our experiences, a habit that has been etched into the mind. A schema sorts information and thus creates order. It also gives us a framework for explaining what we perceive, as well as an action plan for how we should react. We have a schema for riding a bike, for booking our schedules, for eating, etc.

Most of our schemas are effective and useful shortcuts in the mind; the consciousness easily comes up with the right schema when a habit has been automated. But, some schemas return us to emotional patterns we are used to using, but which are not necessarily appropriate.

Let us look at this magical fraction of a second — and at the minutes leading up to it. Here is a traditional behavioural model:

$$Stimulus \Rightarrow Response$$

The extended model says:

$$Stimulus \Rightarrow Choice \Rightarrow Response$$

But we would like to extend the model further:

$$State \; \& \; Choice \; of \; State \Rightarrow Thought \; Seed \; \& \; Emotional \; Seed \Rightarrow Choice \Rightarrow Stimulus \Rightarrow Choice \Rightarrow Response$$

What does this enhanced model entail? At every moment of your life, you are in a certain state. Try to think back on today. You went through a series of different states. Perhaps you were gloomy when you woke up this morning. Perhaps you then had a cup of coffee or went jogging and then felt happier and more clear-headed. Perhaps you were stuck in traffic on your way to work and got annoyed. But then you heard a song on the radio that reminded you of your first love, and you felt cheered and light-hearted. Your state is crucial to how you feel. And it is important to know that your state changes many times throughout the day, and that certain "anchors" (say the smell of coffee, the feeling of claustrophobia, or an old song) can make you go straight from one state to another. (States are made up of three core components — body, language and focus — all of which you can actively affect, ⇨ BODY).

The next stage — thought seeds and emotional seeds — comes before you seriously focus on a thought or emotion. It is at this stage that you can sense what is potentially coming if you continue to give it energy. And it is at this stage that your attention, your con-

At the seed stage, your attention, consciousness and choices can all change direction.

sciousness, and your active choices can all change direction, so that you do not fall back on old and predictable reactions, but take a different path instead.

You can train yourself to be able to feel and evaluate the potential effects of both your state and your thought and emotional seeds. Let's say you stayed up late last night to prepare for today's meeting, but now you find that some of the others hardly bothered preparing. You feel the irritation bubbling inside you. This is the point at which you can actively make a few inner adjustments. For example, you could focus on the values that you honour through your approach (⇨ VALUES), tune in on what you can and cannot influence (⇨ THOUGHTS), or dissociate yourself slightly from the scene, thus changing your

perspective, dampening the irritation, and releasing inner tension (⇨ PERCEPTION, VISION, BODY).

You have a choice, and if you do not make the inner adjustments, you sow certain thought and emotional seeds, and a small stimulus can lead to a strong and undesired (but also predictable) response of yours. By being conscious of your state, you can handle the amygdala hijack at the onset, and thus avoid being hijacked in the first place.

This means that our behaviour is the result of processes that start a lot earlier than the traditional stimulus stage. Hence, to obtain mastery over our behaviour, we must address ourselves to every one of these stages:

① *State*: At this stage you observe. "What is my current state? How do I feel? How is my body? My focus? My inner (and outer) speech? And what do I choose to adjust so as to get into a more constructive and appropriate state?"

② *Thought and emotional seeds*: At this stage you play the Vision and Values keys. You foresee a development and you make a value-based choice. "Which thought and emotional seeds do I sense are beginning to sprout? What would happen if they were given additional nourishment? Which direction would I then take? Is this where I want to go? If not, where would I rather go? What does it take to get me there?"

③ *Choice*: Once you have foreseen your own "automated reaction," you are in a position to choose a different path. It may be that it is not possible for you to suddenly do all this, as if by magic, from one day to the next. But step by step you can grow your ability to be present and wise during these first three steps. Take charge of your own exploration: "What actually helps? What has which effect? Should I withdraw from the situation? Ask for a time-out? Go for a run? Say something else aloud (or inside myself)? Reframe?" Make a choice.

④ *Stimulus*: Thereafter comes the stimulus that you "saw coming," and that you are optimally prepared for. Welcome it! You knew that it would come. You know it. It is a gift for you, because it gives you a chance to practise your new repertoire.

⑤ *Choice*: Once again you choose: "What should my response be? What could be different from what I 'normally' do? How do I make my response and myself unpredictable in a good way, and constructive, so that I have maximum effectiveness and influence? How do I talk my way into the other person's map? How do I remain respectful?"

⑥ *Response*: Now you apply your response. Take note of the effect. Remain in your resourceful state. Be curious and gather experience. Just as the squirrel gathers and hoards nuts, you gather and hoard useful experiences using this model. These are important to remember because they contain learning and suggestions for "more of this next time" or "less of this next time."

It looks complicated, but as you get used to this process, it is actually not that difficult. Of course, you will need to practise, and will probably find yourself being hijacked by your amygdala a couple of times along the way. Old habits are like "motorways" in the brain — and that is why you need some retraining to do something else.

The good thing is that when you recognise the governing

principles of your emotional habits, you no longer need to feel like a helpless victim of the same old reactions. The first step is becoming aware — then can you begin to act differently.

Along the way, remember to sharpen your ability to spot the small nuances in your own development, so that you celebrate your successes and slowly build up new competencies (⇨ GOALS). Know that even when you find yourself on a path you don't like, you can tramp a new path of your own through the forest (⇨ PERCEPTION).

The seahorse in your brain can help you

Approximately 20 per cent of people have an overactive amygdala, which means that their amygdala reacts more frequently than others' do — with fear, elevated heart rate, and feelings of unpleasantness as consequences.

Researchers also know that if a mother is stressed during pregnancy, the child is born with an enlarged amygdala. Therefore, we do not have the same preconditions as one another when it comes to being fearful, and to the size of the amygdala.

Nevertheless, you can affect the size and the activity level of your amygdala today. At this stage, it is useful to know about the hippocampus (Greek for "seahorse," so-named because it actually resembles one). Located in the limbic system, the hippocampus plays a central role in your orientation ability and your memory. If new cells and connections are created in your hippocampus, you have the potential to become smarter and to regulate yourself. Therefore, we want this seahorse to grow.

An inverse relationship exists between the amygdala and the hippocampus.

Anyone who has seen seahorses move knows what a balanced,

calming, soothing, and meditative effect they can have on you. Picture this: Hippocampus — soothing seahorse! Several studies show an inverse proportional relationship between the amygdala and the hippocampus; when one goes up, the other goes down.[25] The amygdala is responsible for subconscious emotional learning, while the hippocampus is responsible for conscious learning.

Due to this inverse proportionality, when you let your hippocampus grow, your amygdala becomes smaller. And the good news is that you can encourage growth in the hippocampus. It grows when you exercise, eat healthy foods, and get enough sleep. It also grows when you meditate.[26] Physical exercise develops a certain chemical growth substance — BDNF — which both **Physical exercise increases** increases the nerve cells' plasticity **nerve cells' plasticity.** and delivers at least 2000 new nerve cells to the hippocampus each day.[27] This may not sound like so much, but when you consider that each nerve cell receives 10,000 connections, there is suddenly room for a lot of new learning.

In other words, being active, harmonious, and upholding healthy habits is a thoroughly good investment that allows you to create "new melodies" each and every day.

Playing the Emotions key

When you play this key, you tune in, like a musician, to your emotions — and to other people's. You notice body language and micro-messages. You become aware of the amygdala's role and the potential draining of resourcefulness. You know that all emotions are latently present all the time, that they are closely connected to all the other keys, and that which emotions you have right now very much comes down to your choice. You also know how easily emotions are transferred from one person to another,

and you explore how playing the other seven keys on your inner piano can create a change of emotion. You are aware of your magical fraction of a second and deal with it wisely.

You know too neurons that fire together, wire together. This is true in relation to negative life events (such as the shrimp episode after which you became ill). But it is fortunately also true in relation to positive events. Think of a person you like, and your brain will fire emotions accordingly. Create a situation, or do an activity you like, and positive emotions fire again. You cannot command yourself to be happy, but you can think or do things that make you happy and thus create positive spirals of emotions.

Musicians build up their ability to change emotions quickly. They move rapidly between different expressions within the same piece of music. They thus have the power to "pick" and enter the emotions most useful for the expression of the music. They can be contemplative one second, longing the next, then furious, and happy and released in the end. This takes a high level of emotional flexibility. As C.P.E. Bach wrote, "A musician cannot move others unless he too is moved."[28] The same goes for powerful communication elsewhere. If you want others to feel your message, feel it yourself. The mirror neurons in the room will then do their job and make the emotions contagious.

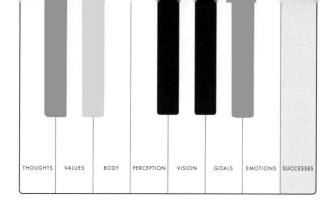

| THOUGHTS | VALUES | BODY | PERCEPTION | VISION | GOALS | EMOTIONS | SUCCESSES |

8

Successes

Tapping into your achievements

WE ALL HAVE a deep reservoir of experiences; it holds important knowledge of our best practices and successes. Yet we often treat this reservoir as a graveyard rather than a source of life. Performers and musicians at the top of their game, however, know that the reservoir can be infinitely drawn upon, to inspire new and greater performances. You may need a "clue" to revisit relevant experiences — but they are there. Solutions, insights and strategies will surface when you trust that the brain will do its job and go searching. Instead of starting from scratch when you want to create change — or seeking to copy-and-paste other people's strategies — you can tap into your past achievements, build a resourceful state from there, and draw the most useful inspiration for current and future strategies. Let's see how that works.

A manager once brought a difficult conversation with an employee to the table in coaching. "I have no idea how to tackle this," he said, shaking his head. The alarm bell of his brain, the amygdala, had clearly been activated: "It's a new situation; I feel stuck; I don't see a way out. It's a threat to me." His system was on high alert.

Instead of giving him a quick-fix answer, the coach steered him towards reflection: "Think of a 'difficult conversation' you've had before with an employee — and handled successfully."

This invitation led to an introspective pause, followed by a big smile indicating an insight, and then an account of what had worked back then. The insight completely turned the conversation around, and put the manager in touch with his vigour.

What worked well in the past? And how do I make use of the best of that experience?

Suddenly he became aware that he had been in a similar situation two years ago — not completely identical to this one, but with many similar elements. "And then I did x, y, and z, and that worked well...."

By prompting him to revisit a successful experience, the coach had offered a so-called "clue" to his brain. Knowing that everything ever said and all questions ever asked rest on assumptions anyway, the coach chose to assume that there had been similar, successful situations which had resulted in useful learning, and that the manager was indeed capable of retrieving them.

An approach full of faith

This approach — full of faith in his ability and the value of his experiences — put the manager into contact with successful strategies lying dormant inside him. Suddenly, he was on a different "hunt" than before. Instead of focusing on "How on earth do

I tackle this difficult conversation?" he went to "What worked well in the past, and how do I make use of the best of that experience, adapting it to the current situation?" He became resourceful instantly.

When applying this method yourself, there are several areas to explore after you have gotten into contact with one of your successes. You may, for instance, ask:

- How did I prepare for the conversation back then?
- Which of my values shone the brightest?
- What did I think about the situation?
- What did I know beforehand about the employee and his/her world?
- Who helped me?
- Which of my resources did I use?
- What was my key to success? If it were formulated as a recipe, what would it look like?
- Was there anything that did not work so well, and which should be avoided this time?
- What should be added this time, that was not there last time?
- How can my strategy be pieced together in the most powerful way?
- So what are my next steps, bearing this learning in mind?

The manager in the above example could well have gone from advisor to advisor and gotten all kinds of answers. Lots of people do this, essentially taking a "lifetime subscription" to external advisors. But this would merely have strengthened his belief that the answer to this challenge was to be found outside of him. His "external reference" would have grown (⇨ GOALS).

By drawing on his own experience, however, and playing the

Successes key, he instead strengthens his "internal reference"— and self-reliance — an investment of a lifetime.

When you can recognise patterns and best practices in your life and absorb knowledge from the situations you are in and have been in, you will be able to use core elements of the successes across situations too. And you will strengthen your ability to cope with the things that went less well.

If the manager had not accessed this learning, his successful experience from back then would gradually have lost colour and definition. That is the logic of the brain: use it or lose it. Therefore, learn from what works well in your life — not in order to compile a cookbook of "must-do procedures," but instead to wisely make the most of your experiences while flexibly and creatively adapting yourself to future situations.

A reservoir of experience

Most of us seem to notice when things go wrong — a failed conversation, a lost opportunity, a hasty action regretted. We feel tormented by these experiences; we do not know how to put them to rest and they keep coming back again and again, making us feel humiliated, embarrassed, angry. Furthermore, we may acknowledge our big successes in life, but we overlook the smaller ones. We recognise the success and greatness of others, but feel inadequate in comparison.[1]

In this chapter, the focus is on the many successes *we* have had, big or small, that we are not aware of because they dwell in the subconscious parts of the brain. All this "tacit knowledge" is just waiting to be accessed and activated. When the activation takes place you build an enormous bank of meaningful knowledge and successful strategies. It is a powerful and cheap way of creating competency development.

In this way you use what researchers also call "intelligent memory," in which analysis and intuition walk hand in hand, making the most of the slow and the fast systems of the brain (⇨VISION). You recall and learn, in various combinations — your mind wanders from piece to piece of the puzzle until, in a flash, it sees what to do — and it is a powerful way of getting you going.[2]

The more you approach life in this way, the more you build up faith in your ability to find important answers and opportunity by learning from your own rich reservoir of experiences. And the more you look for successes, the more you will find.

Making your skills transferable

People can be good at something in one situation and yet be completely lousy at the same thing in other situations. It often comes down to their not realising that their skills are transferable. With some effort you can apply a skill in a new environment, to a new situation. But it may never happen until you start paying attention to the "paradoxes" of your life.

One such "paradox" was found in a businesswoman who knew she was creative in her spare time — she was a talented amateur painter — but did not consider herself creative at work. Why? Because she had the habit of paying attention to how different the situations were — negotiating and managing projects at work, versus standing in front of the canvas at home. However, when she started exploring the key process of her creativity, and the similarities of the situations, she got to "Aha!" She first identified the kind of questions she would ask herself while being in her creative flow. Then she translated these questions into the professional realm — what

You can apply your skills in new environments, to new situations.

would a similar process look and sound like at work? The context differed, yes, the materials differed, yes, the words of the questions asked differed, yes, but there were patterns in how she approached situations. For instance she came to realise that she did indeed use both the slow and the fast mental systems in her approach to things (⇨GOALS): zooming in on (and analysing) the specific elements available; zooming out and seeing the bigger picture and purpose. Focussing and letting go of focus, like ebb and flow, created a unique and highly flexible and creative mindset, whether she was at home or at work. This created a big "Aha!" moment for her. And it made her understand how to use her resources to apply her full ability across different situations and environments.

No matter the challenge at hand, you can always learn from your successes. One caution though: If your goal is to create an innovative, out-of-the-box product (say, a new kitchen tool), then you do not want to deliberately enliven the *result* of an old success in that field (say, another kitchen tool). This is likely to create a "functional fixation"— applying the exact same strategy, even though it is not useful. You may still, however, want to learn from the most innovative processes you have ever come across or been part of. The focus here is thus on processes, not results: What *enabled* the innovation? Which forms of interaction and processes ignited the flame? How many were present—and with which roles, etc.? There will always be useful learning to harvest from successful processes from the past.

When playing this key, do remember the wisdom of Heraclitus, the ancient Greek philosopher: "No man ever steps in the same river twice, for it's not the same river and he's not the same man."

All that knowledge, just waiting for a clue

Our brains work by the "use it or lose it" principle: what we use grows stronger, what we do not use fades away.

Furthermore, what is not kept alive loses its "clue." The crucial connection between our conscious memory and the particular experience is then lost — at least temporarily. Forgetting is actually not a question of decay; it is rather the lack of clues. The memory is always present, but the connections are temporarily broken. You probably know what it is like to forget someone's name. "That tall guy with dark hair, who drives the little red car — what was his name again?" you ask yourself while your nerve cells are firing at full speed. And then you get a clue: "His first name starts with an 'O'... Of course — Oscar!"

When we learn something new it is consolidated in our memory. But we also forget, often because we have not used this memory for a while. A clue can stir your memory, provided you are dealing with something that was indeed learned and encoded (some people listen so superficially when others introduce themselves that they would never be able to recall the names).

It is worth knowing that successful experiences are consolidated with positive emotions in your emotional memory. When these successes are remembered, it strengthens their existence, and they can be remembered particularly easily when you are in touch with similar emotions. In other words, successful experiences are best remembered when you are

Successful experiences are best remembered when you are happy.

happy and optimistic, and thus harder to recall when you are feeling down. Therefore, if you want to go hunting for your successes, pay attention to your mood. A positive emotion will work as a clue for the brain. If you are in a bad mood — and do not

seem to be able to switch away from it in the minutes to come — wait. It is no wonder that things, including your experiences and your abilities, seem rather grey and dull right now. This will change, because states do change. And when you start feeling lighter and happier, then start playing your Successes key.

Language creates our world

"Language does not describe reality," wrote Ludwig Wittgenstein, "Language creates it." These are extremely important words to remember when we play the Successes key.

Questions open one world and close off another. And you will gain very different effects depending on whether you ask open or closed questions (⇨THOUGHTS).

- "Do you have any resources you can use?" is a
  closed question that sets up a yes/no answer.
- "Which of your resources can you use?" is an
  open question.

The risks of a closed question reveal themselves when the answer given is "No." This "No" does not necessarily tell the truth about the state of resourcefulness; it could in fact just be down to:

- An inner search that was too narrow (say, if the manager mentioned at the beginning of the chapter had searched his brain exclusively for "difficult conversations with employees");
- Impatience (if the manager had not reflected long enough to realise which resources could be usefully applied);
- Inexperience with the process (if the manager had not trusted the process, and not believed that successful experiences would show up);

⊙ Lack of self-confidence (if the manager had not thought
of himself as sufficiently competent).

No matter the reason for a "No" answer to a closed question,
if you answer "No," you have painted yourself into a corner.

By contrast, asking the open question of which resources can
be used signals your faith that there are indeed useful resources
available, and that it is simply a matter of finding them.

The importance of insights

"The penny dropped." "I had an epiphany." "That was a
revelation."

These are many ways of saying the same thing: I had an
insight! The pattern is well-known. We experience a dilemma,
we reflect, we obtain some insight, we become enthusiastic, and
then we are motivated to act. An insight was what the manager
got when he realised he could access and make use of that particular experience of his to solve his current problem.

Insights put the brain's neurotransmitters and modulators into
action. They kick-start the nerve cells and provide better opportunities for exploiting the brain's capacity. At the same time, they
give you the power to eliminate natural opposition to change.
The experience of insight is so very pleasant that the number of
brain waves at the gamma level increases.[3] This is a sign that the
various parts of the brain are working together optimally.

But let's step backwards for a moment. Just before the attain-
ment of insight comes a period of reflection. This reflection
increases the frequency of brain waves at the alpha level, which
are associated with the relaxation and balance that ensue from
inward attention and mindfulness. At the same time, serotonin,
a neurotransmitter that increases relaxation and relieves pain, is
released.[4]

This process occurs during reflection, but does not occur when you are involved in problem-solving — when your thinking is analytical, your attention is focused, and your slow system is working hard. At such times, alpha activity actually drops, and beta activity increases.

Ideas pop up when the brain is put into neutral.[5] The road towards an epiphany therefore does not pass through beta, but through alpha. So, similar to what we wrote in the Thoughts key, when you have to make a decision, you should collect information, then invite the Body key to play along, by taking a walk, "forgetting" it, sleeping on it.

Ideas pop up when the brain is put into neutral — so, go for a walk, or sleep on it.

Have faith in the fast, subconscious system. Feed it with open, inquisitive questions, playing your Thoughts key — and wait for the answer. It will come!

That is why a person who forces himself to stay in the overly concentrated problem-solving mode will not reach an insight. Trying too hard and expecting too much blocks insights.[6] Your good intentions thus become counterproductive, because they are not in line with brain logic. Learn to let your mind wander — "space out" a little!

Elite athletes emit alpha waves in their brains just before an excellent performance.[7] In that state, they are focused, calm, and at one with their bodies and their experience; their inner dialogue is quieted. To what extent does your everyday life allow you to go into an alpha-state? How much do you consciously use alpha to attain a sudden insight?

As we discuss in earlier chapters, when you give orders to yourself, or receive orders from others, those regions of the brain associated with the amygdala are activated. A warning lamp in the prefrontal area of your brain lights up, and induces a condition where you look for errors in the orders given. In other words, you mobilise your inner defence mechanism.

On the other hand, when you are invited, by yourself or by others, to "think along" in the change process, something completely different happens. Reflection levels rise. Insights appear. And your inner motivation increases.

So, the next time when you feel like just *telling* yourself what needs to be done, pause for a moment. It is at this very point that giving yourself room for reflection can generate that crucial leap to valuable insight.

The structure of your good habits

One way to play the Successes key is to look at the structure of what works for you — your good habits. Always start here when you want to change a bad habit or develop a new good habit.

This exercise gives you access to the tacit knowledge about what works for you already, because your good habits are likely to have certain structures, and these are strong motivators for action.

This exercise consists of five steps:

① Fill in the following form with as many of your good habits as you can think of.

② For each habit, ask yourself, "Which higher goals does each habit serve?" Also include results reached, values honoured, etc.

③ Now ask yourself, "When did I initiate what came to be a good habit?"

④ Then ask yourself, "What do I tell myself today that helps me maintain this good habit?" Write down examples of your inner dialogue.

Good habit	What higher goals does the habit serve?	When did I initiate it?	What do I tell myself that helps me maintain it?
Planning my next day before leaving the office	• *Overview* • *Focus* • *Prioritisation* • *Inner calm* • *Flexibility*	*2006*	• *"First closure, then leisure."* • *"It feels great to have the big overview."* • *"Knowing my priorities gives me flexibility."*
A run each morning	• *Energy* • *Focus* • *Freedom* • *Inner calm*	*2002*	• *"A kickstart is a great start."* • *"I invest in my day, in my relations, my well-being."*
Listening (and asking) before speaking my mind	• *Insight* • *Curiosity* • *Overview* • *Freedom* • *Flexibility*	*1985*	• *"What (more exactly) does he/she mean?"* • *"If I don't get the situation, I won't hit home."*
Parachuting hobby	• *Freedom* • *Energy* • *Curiosity* • *Inner calm*	*1991*	• *"How different the world can look!"* • *"Free as a bird."*

What do the good habits seem to have in common?

Certain values seem to motivate and work for me: freedom, flexibility, curiosity, energy. There is playfulness in my choice of words. My inner dialogue focuses on the activities' higher aims — and joy.

⑤ Then zoom out to a "helicopter perspective" and look at your responses from a distance: "What do the good habits seem to have in common?" Write it at the bottom of the form.

The exercise shows you the traits that are present in and crucial to what you do well, and to your motivation. It also enables the understanding that the same purpose can be achieved in numerous ways. It deals with shaping your new habits in the light of what works well for you.

Prime your brain for successful change

When playing the Successes key, always look for what works well. If you have a habit that you want changed, then first comprehend the structure of your good habits as shown above.

When you have a challenge and feel stuck or anxious, then start by absorbing the learning from a situation where you were successful. That will make your amygdala relax. It does not have to be a situation that is very similar to your current one. A few recognisable aspects are enough.

When you work this way, you are priming your brain. Priming means that one stimulus affects the response to a later stimulus. The stimulus of doing this exercise will positively influence how you respond to challenging situations in the future.

When you enter a supermarket and smell freshly baked bread, it increases your likelihood of ending up buying freshly baked bread. That first stimulus (the smell) affects the choice you later make.

When you deliberately invite a successful stimulus to enter your mind, you strengthen your belief that "Of course I can deal with such things successfully." This affects your later response. And when you start looking systematically for successes, you

sow important seeds in your mind; more successes will sprout, and you will notice and learn.

Priming is an example of latent learning. The information that you receive keeps working inside of you even though you are not aware of it. We are here referring to subconscious memory processes that particularly concern emotional reactions and opinions. When you influence yourself with an optimistic feeling, with possible solutions, and with belief in your abilities, you rise to the challenge of effecting positive change.

Growth mindset vs. fixed mindset

Another way of boosting your own successes is by applying a "growth mindset."

Take a look at the equation below: How much of IQ is due to hard work, and how much is due to genetics?

$$IQ = (\quad)\% \text{ hard work} + (\quad)\% \text{ genetics}$$

The psychologists Mueller and Dweck carried out this test with students and found that those with what they labelled a "fixed mindset" thought that genetics would be more important than hard work, that intelligence is predominantly dependent on a set ability determined at birth; by contrast, people with a "growth mindset" considered intelligence something that involves knowledge, know-how, and hard work.[8] These two mindsets can determine to what extent we develop as human beings.[9]

As specialised skills and expertise do not demand an IQ of more than 120, if one wants to go far, it very much comes down to hard work and commitment. This does not preclude that people with higher IQ can go further, but hard work is the main factor.[10] In fact, faith in one having a high IQ can lead to complacency.

Dweck further showed that children with a growth mindset get more out of education and enjoy greater success than children with a fixed mindset.[11] She carried out a very thought-provoking experiment with children.[12] The kids solved a problem and were then praised by the researchers with a single sentence. Half of them were praised for their intelligence; the other half were praised for their effort. Afterwards, the children chose a new assignment — either one that was harder than the first, but which they were told they would learn a lot from, or an easy task that was on the same level as the one they had just solved. Ninety per cent of the children who had been praised for their effort chose the challenging assignment, while most children who were praised for their intelligence chose the easy one. Dweck was surprised, and concluded that when we praise children for their intelligence, we simultaneously signal that they do not need to take any risks.

Children with a growth mindset enjoy greater success than those with a fixed mindset.

The next step in Dweck's experiment showed that fear of failure inhibits learning. The same children were now given a new test — one designed for children three years older than they. Dweck wanted to see how the subjects would react to this challenge. The children who had been praised for their intelligence were easily scared off. They interpreted their first, unavoidable mistake as "failure," and began to doubt themselves: "Perhaps I am not that smart after all?" They preferred to compare themselves with those children who had performed worse on the test. By contrast, the children who had been praised for their effort got heavily involved. "This is my favourite test," some of them even said. They also demonstrated great curiosity towards the children who had done better. They wanted to understand and

learn from their mistakes, and figure out how they could perform better the next time.

In the final round of tests, the difficulty level was the same as in the first problem. And the results were striking. The children who had continuously been praised for their effort had improved by 30 per cent. And, astoundingly, those who had been praised for their intelligence performed 20 per cent worse! The risk of making a mistake had influenced them so much that they experienced a setback in their problem-solving abilities. It is also not unthinkable that their inner dialogue had been self-critical and extensive (⇨THOUGHTS), taking up space in the working memory they needed badly in order to perform.

Think of the relevance of this experiment to you now. Try to put it in the context of inner/outer motivation (⇨GOALS), of your own development process: Do you aim to make the grade or to push the boundaries?

The good news is that you can learn to develop a growth mindset. You can learn to believe in yourself, and to embrace situations as being changeable and possible rather than static.

The knowledge society we live in today puts the spotlight on knowledge development, creativity, and innovation. Therefore, we must evaluate people in other ways than what we are used to. Instead of making a distinction between high and low intelligence, strong and weak skills, success and failure, personality profiles, etc., a more useful distinction is between those people who are quick to learn and those who are slow to learn. Dweck's research conclusively shows that people who are quick to learn have a growth mindset, and the ones who are slow to learn have a fixed mindset. Therefore, we need to promote growth mindsets — and to prevent and convert fixed mindsets.

So, how does a fixed mindset come about? After all, all small children are, by nature, endowed with insatiable curiosity and a unique motivation to learn. Life is a learning process in itself. Children learn to walk; they fall but get up again; they make mistakes but they try again — from the beginning. But, it is possible to "deflate the balloon," so to speak, because mindsets are culturally hereditary. Adult mindsets rub off on children. There are plenty of examples showing how fixed mindsets are created. Tell the child that he is stupid, that he is clumsy, that he is full of flaws and shortcomings. Tell him that there is a lot he will never be able to learn, that he is incompetent. Or, make him scared of not being smart enough, by evaluating his performance constantly. Tell him what is right and wrong, and always elevate academic knowledge above personal development. Then the fixed mindset will be swiftly and firmly in place....

What should the child learn instead, so as to be ready for the future? He should develop a growth mindset by learning:

- To love challenges, instead of thinking that they are difficult and hard.
- To make an effort, instead of thinking that things happen by themselves.
- To be steadfast in the face of hardships, instead of bending like a frail straw.
- That mistakes lead to success, instead of thinking that mistakes are dangerous or wrong.

But first and foremost, the child must learn to know himself!

More of what works, please!

It makes sense to look for what worked in past, and to build bridges to your learning and your constructive experiences. That which you focus on, you nourish. That which you nourish, grows. And that which grows, becomes your reality.

Since its birth, psychology has primarily focused on what did not work in people, and how that could be handled. Causes, diagnoses, and treatments are central here. For several generations it did not occur to the psychologist community as a whole to look for what was already good, and to explore how it might become even better.

It was the American psychologist Martin Seligman who, in the early 1990s, properly defined the need for a field that focused on improving the mental functionality of healthy people. He called this field "positive psychology." Among other things, he writes in his book, *Learned Optimism*:

> *Psychology had taught us a great deal about pathology, suffering, victims, and how one acquires one's proficiency to combat sadness and anxiety. Meanwhile, the discovery of the skills necessary for becoming happier was relegated to amusement parks, Hollywood, and beer commercials.*[13]

This more constructive approach to life looks at resilience, or the "bounce-back ability"—how people regain balance when challenged. The basic premise of coaching and self-coaching is a deeply rooted faith in people's intrinsic resources and in their ability to formulate effective paths of development, looking at the glass as half-full, not half-empty.

Still, much homespun psychology is influenced by the traditional psychological focus: "What is the problem/matter?" "For how long have you felt like this" "What is the reason for your problem – what is it down to?" Many of us tap into this tradition by default in our everyday life. The intentions are undoubtedly good – but attention is thus led to what we want less of, thereby paradoxically creating more of it (⇨ VISION).

Playing the Successes key

This is a great key to finish off with. Playing the Successes key will build you up. You will learn, naturally, from tacit knowledge and situations you did not think of revisiting systematically before. You will start noticing many more successful experiences because you look for them. You will build up beliefs that you can do it — and that you have valuable answers and solutions at hand inside of you. Every new situation contains potential learning; your life becomes an adventure worth participating in!

Every new situation contains potential learning.

If you represent an organisation, this is the key that can offer you the most competency development — for free. Harnessing the many successes you have in your everyday organisational life, learning across individuals and teams, and priming yourself for future successes, are some of the empowering side-effects this will bring you. Becoming an insight-generating organisation is a powerful way to enter the future — allowing room to reflect and stimulate, deliberately oscillating between the slow and the fast system of the brain, thus coming up with new and powerful answers to the questions of our time.

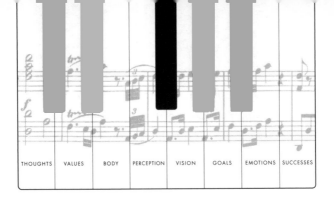

| THOUGHTS | VALUES | BODY | PERCEPTION | VISION | GOALS | EMOTIONS | SUCCESSES |

9

All together now!

Playing the keys, creating the change

YOU HAVE NOW DONE a lot of good thinking, and have learned that you know much more than you think because the brain has an ability to discover new patterns of meaning within the information it already possesses. This process is your brain's inner music, playing all day long, and even when you are sleeping — offering new ideas and insights for you to catch.

Change is possible because your brain is plastic. Pioneers in the field have known and described this plasticity for decades,[1] but it has only been accepted by the scientific community in the last 20 years.

There is an ongoing neuroplasticity taking place, and it is enhanced when you play your brain. By knowing and playing the eight keys on your inner piano — and switching focus when you

feel stuck on one of them — you train your brain to deliberately shift perspective and find new ways to create resourcefulness. By playing your brain in musical ways, you "tramp new neural paths in the forest"; you get to strengthen those connections of value to you and your surroundings — and you apply the playful approach that enables you to return to the desired path and keep going, with a twinkle in your eye.

As we have seen, "cells that fire together, wire together"; your actions today create and constantly reinforce a hard-wired truth inside you. But it is also true that "cells that fire apart, wire apart," giving us hope that we *can* break free of these ingrained habits by deliberately changing our attention.

With some training, your brain will be able to "fire" this self-regulating approach when you want to create change. The impetus may be that you feel trapped, depressed, annoyed, or that you desire new opportunities or aspire to higher dreams. In other words, it is possible to turn the "change wanted" state into a trigger for active and constructive self-regulation.

Consolidating the musical mindset

This book has brought together brain knowledge and a musical mindset as a method for effecting successful change in your life and career. The brain knowledge is in the keys of your inner piano — you know what they are good for, and why they are important. The musical mindset lies in *how* you play the keys, and is characterised by ten core assets:

① *Skilled* — you know each individual key through
   curiosity and practice, and build a broad repertoire;
② *Synergistic* — you know the importance of making
   the keys sound together;

③ *Structured yet spontaneous* — you are capable of
following the score as well as improvising creatively;

④ *Flexible* — you adapt to the demands of the situation
and surroundings, and do so with a good sense of
timing;

⑤ *Resilient* — you quickly bounce back onto track when
a mistake is made;

⑥ *Oscillating between experience and analysis* — you use the
appropriate brain system (fast vs. slow) in the
relevant situations;

⑦ *Collaborative* — you have the socio-emotional skills to
play together with others to create a unique whole;

⑧ *Present* — you absorb yourself into the activity at hand,
creating "flow" and top performances;

⑨ *Playful* — you approach life with optimism, humour,
joy, and a spirit of experimentation;

⑩ *Patient* — you know that mastery does not come
overnight, that all beginnings are difficult, and that
results will come in time.

There is music in the brain, music in the way you play your
brain, and music in any kind of social interaction. What really
matters in communication is listening and leadership, a sense of
when to listen and when to take the lead. Just like a musician in
a jazz band, you can grow your ability to nurture group coordination and fluency in your daily communication and interaction.

Prepare to play

You now know what each individual key is called and what it rep-
resents. Perhaps you are already aware of which keys you play
often — and which you are barely acquainted with. You have
worked with your inner piano keys one at a time, since this is

how the brain's slow system operates, thoroughly and in detail.

Now you need to find your own melody, and all the keys must come into play. The eight keys — the octave of your inner piano — can create a vast number of new melodies. In fact, any good music must be an innovation, as Les Baxter, the American musician and composer, put it.

To begin playing your inner piano is to practise your musicality and to train your ear — your ability to combine the keys and listen to how they chime in concert.

The brain's slow system thinks through *exclusion* — one thing at a time. The fast system thinks through *inclusion* — all the keys taken together. There are thoughts in emotions and values in perception. In the best of all worlds, there are goals in visions and visions in goals. The body is a part of all of this. And you have successes within all of the remaining keys — as well as in numerous other areas of life.

This form of thinking is called complexity thinking. It can only be explained when we regard the brain as a network, and the most important prerequisite for being able to do this is time. The musician is trained to think in time. In fact, timing is crucial. And it is the foundation for the interaction of all the keys on your inner piano too.

Create synergies with your keys

Now it is time to play the keys together. You are ready to experience different ways of using the keys and the insights of this book. We suggest you start with these three exercises: (1) Observing the current habits of your inner piano and learning from them; (2) experimenting with the interplay of your eight keys; and (3) dealing with a particular challenge or with a particular area of your life in which you seek change.

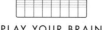

The current habits of your inner piano

Which key(s) are you most familiar with today? What focus grows from that? What do you miss by focusing so much on this/ these? Which do you play the least? What might you gain from getting to know these? What would you hear that you have not heard before?

The interplay of your keys

How many fingers do you currently play with? One? Two? Three? More? If you find yourself feeling stuck playing one or two keys, try experimenting with some of the others — and see where that takes you.

How quickly can you move from one key to another? What reminds you to change key? How do you make sure you do it? How do, say, three keys sound when you play them together? You have lots of options here — so there is a plenty of opportunity for experimentation.

Think of one of the eight keys that we have dealt with in this book. Let's say you choose "Thoughts." First, repeat the key's distinctive features. This is a strategy for the brain's slow system. Then connect the brain's fast system, so that you become aware of how working with Thoughts affects the other keys. For instance, critical inner dialogue affects your Emotions and Body straight away. You may use visualisation to create silence in your head, a "thoughtless," mindful, and powerful awareness. These are examples of how Thoughts are intertwined with other keys.

You can get more Aha's by reflecting likewise upon the other keys: How does this key relate to the other keys? When brought together, what becomes possible? In which parts of my life would it be useful to play them together?

Dealing with a particular challenge

Write down a topic you would like to coach yourself on (say, "My relationship with my boss," or "Prepare for the meeting on Wednesday.") Write down a particular goal you would like to achieve (say "Come up with three options of dealing with him" or "Make a five-point plan"). Choose a particular order for the eight keys you are going to play — write it down. Now "visit" each and every key while you write down the insights you get, as you go along. Some relevant questions to ask yourself in relation to each key could be:

THOUGHTS

- How does my inner dialogue sound currently? How does it affect me?
- What is the nature of the questions I ask myself? What would a switch from "closed" to "open" questions give? How would such empowering open questions sound?
- Where do I focus my attention?
- If I am in "Judger" mode, what would a switch to "Observer" or "Learner" produce?
- What can I influence, what can I not influence?
- What does the narrative I strengthen with my thoughts sound like? Which stories do I repeatedly tell myself and how do they affect me?

VALUES

- Which values are core to me?
- Which values do I particularly want to honour in this relationship/situation/meeting? No matter what happens exactly, which values will I stay true to?

- What are the values of the other person, the participants, the organisation?
- What are my behavioural evidences of value X — and what may be the behavioural evidences of the other(s)?
- What are my "towards" goals and what are my "away from" goals in this? What am I attracted to, and what do I want to shun?
- What is of short-term value versus long-term value to me — and to us — in this?

BODY

- What is my state like when I am very resourceful? What does my Pyramid of Success (Body, Focus, Language) look like? Likewise: What does my Pyramid of Failure look like? How do they compare?
- How am I breathing? Adjust it appropriately to make it more supportive.
- How is my body behaving when I think of this person/ relationship/situation? Make relevant adjustments to your body, and enter your resourceful Pyramid of Success, imagining that you cope with the person/ relationship/situation in this state.
- What do I do with my body right now? Where can I use it actively? When can I take a break and do something else?
- Who do I know who masters what I would like to do? What are their secrets? What would I learn if I asked them? What would I see (and my mirror neurons copy) if I saw them while doing this?

PERCEPTION

- How do I frame the event/the person/myself/the relationship? — give your framing a title! Which effects does it have, and how useful are these effects? Which effects would I rather see? Which alternative framings would further these effects? — give them titles, taste them, and make your choice!
- What does this look like from the First, Second and Third positions respectively?
- How might a complete stranger frame this relationship/situation if viewed from their neutral place?
- What new paths would I like to tramp in the forest?
- How would a Robinson Crusoe reframing look like? What are the positive side-effects of something — anything? Go from a pessimistic perception of things to an optimistic one.

VISION

- Which system am I using the most currently — the slow, analytical one, or the fast, intuitive one? Do I apply them relevantly to simple/complex tasks? If not, what change is needed?
- What do I see and which emotions does that vision awaken inside of me?
- In the best of all worlds, how would this relationship be? How would this meeting go?
- What would a mind sculpture of this situation look like? Imagine yourself in the situation, bringing to life vision, emotions, sounds, smells, tastes! Conduct a mental rehearsal where you — in your resourceful state — animate your goals and opportunities in the situation.

⊙ How does this add to the bigger agenda of my life, the organisation, the relationship?

⊙ Ten years from now, when I look back on this relationship/situation, what will I have learnt that is of value?

GOALS

⊙ What is my vision, and what are my "towards" goals in relation to this relationship/situation? The more attention focused here, the stronger the brain circuits! How will I know the vision has come alive and the goals are reached? Make your goals specific and with a definite time frame, and write them down! Use the Goal Checklist.

⊙ What characterises my motivation right now? Is it of inner or outer nature? How may I switch from outer to inner — and thus enhance my level of motivation?

⊙ How can I break my goal down into small steps that make me more resourceful and the goal more attainable and less daunting? How might a Habit Tracker help me monitor my progress? How could I use it?

⊙ How can I best apply crammed practice (good for short-term learning) and spaced practice (good for long-term learning)?

EMOTIONS

⊙ Which emotions do I want to infect this relationship/situation with? Being aware of my body language, which micro-messages will I aim to send out?

⊙ How do I bring to life the emotions I want? All emotions are latently present at all times. When you focus on a particular emotion, you get more of it! Beware of your level of rapport with yourself right now. What will it take to tune in and tap into your resourcefulness?

⊙ What are my amygdala habits? Bearing in mind that the amygdala stores emotional experiences at low resolution — what less-resourceful memories may be triggered in this situation and thus cause uncalled-for anger/fear?

⊙ Bearing in mind that emotion can hijack me and that I have a magical fraction of a second to do something else, where do I want to build up my repertoire? In which of these stages?

State & Choice of State ⇨ *Thought Seed & Emotional Seed* ⇨ *Choice* ⇨ *Stimulus* ⇨ *Choice* ⇨ *Response*

SUCCESSES

⊙ When have I been in similar situations/relationships before where I coped well? What were the keys to success there? What did I do to understand the person(s)/ situation(s)? How did I prepare?

⊙ How can I take the best from these and apply it now, while staying open to the uniqueness of this situation/ relationship and new approaches?

⊙ Which of my many resources can I apply to this relationship/situation? What would that give to the other(s), and add to the bigger picture?

⊙ What is my mood right now? Successful experiences are best remembered when you are happy. Ideas pop up when the brain is put into neutral. Gather information and "forget it," sleep on it. Have faith in the fast, intuitive,

and subconscious system. Feed it with open, curious questions — and wait for the answer. It will come!

- What is the structure of my good habits? What is the structure of something positive that already works in my life? In what ways does this prepare me for the relationship/situation?
- How is my mindset right now? Is it "fixed," or is it oriented towards "growth" and constant learning?

After having been inspired by these questions and requests, now try to challenge yourself even more:

- Play the keys again, only faster this time.
- Play the keys again, but in a different order.
- Play the keys again, now combining two or more keys while you play — see what comes up, and write it down.

As you become more skilled, you may not have to define a particular order. You can start to play by ear!

An example of how to keep playing

Starting out with the "problem" brought up in the Thoughts chapter — "I am lonely" — how might you play the keys on your inner piano? Which questions would be useful and relevant to ask? What do they do? Where do they take you?

The example that follows shows how several keys can be played together. It is meant as inspiration, not an answer book, so go ahead and improvise, play variations, make it your own.

Thoughts: My problem is that I am lonely.

Vision: My dream is to connect with other people in meaningful ways; to interact. (Already, you have switched from your "problem lenses" to "dream lenses.")

Now, feed your inner play with a series of open questions:

Keys	Questions to ask	Gains
VALUES + VISION	• What type of interaction do I dream of? • With what kind of people? • Sharing which values and interests? • What makes the dream important to me?	*Understanding the dream*
EMOTIONS + BODY	• How does this dream make me feel? • How does it show in my body? • How do I act?	*Contact with emotions*
PERCEPTION + VALUES + EMOTIONS	• What would make me a most attractive person to be with in the eyes of other people; person A, B, C? • Which of my values and traits shine through here — and how does that make me feel?	*New perspective*
GOAL	• What is my concrete goal: How often, in what way, and with whom do I really dream of interacting?	*Calibration[2]*
ALL KEYS	• What characterises a most useful state for me when I connect with people? • What is my Pyramid of Success and how do I apply it?	*Adjustment of the state*

Keys	Questions to ask	Gains
SUCCESSES	• When in my life have I connected and interacted most meaningfully with other people? • What was present then? • Which of my resources did I draw upon?	*Contact with successful experiences and internal resource identification*
THOUGHTS + BODY	• What is my inner dialogue like when I think about this? • How does it show in my body? • What happens if I change the speed of my inner dialogue? • Which small changes would make me more resourceful?	*Boosting the inner dialogue*
VISION + VALUES	• Who could help me achieving this dream? • Who would I like to see in the picture apart from myself? What would they gain? And what would we create — in synergy? • What valuable would that add to the process?	*External resource identification*
THOUGHTS + GOALS	• What can stop me pursuing this dream? • And how do I navigate around that?	*Identification of barriers and the making of a Plan B*

Keys	Questions to ask	Gains
VISION	• Looking at the dream and the road towards it: which good options for meaningful inter- action do I have?	*Identification of opportunities*
PERCEPTION + THOUGHTS	• If everyone keeps doing what they have always done, what can I then do differently? • What would it be useful to interpret this as, to create and maintain momentum?	*Reframing and activation of personal responsibility*
SUCCESSES	• What seems to work well for me when I pursue a dream? • How do I take that into ac-count when making a plan?	*Creating a plan that suits one's own mental maps*
GOAL	• Which small step(s) can I take today to get closer to my dream? • What is my plan? When do I do what? What will remind me? How will I hold myself accountable?	*Action!*

Play your brain and enjoy the play! Applying a musical mind-set will help you test out various tunes in an unprejudiced way and keep going, keep trying — knowing it will come.

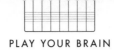

Structuring the play on your inner piano

We are all different and what works for one person may not be the best for another. When you start coaching yourself, do be aware of the range of choices you have:

- ◉ Perhaps you prefer to coach yourself orally, by asking questions out loud or mentally, and letting them take shape as you go along?

- ◉ Perhaps you would rather coach yourself in writing, by writing down your questions, whether before you begin or as you go along — and writing your way towards your realisations?

- ◉ Perhaps your processes are of a more visual or kinaesthetic kind?

- ◉ Perhaps you present yourself with an important question to consider? "What do I infect others with?" or "When do we create the best results in the department?" And then you let your brain chew on it and look for answers in your daily life.

- ◉ Perhaps you collect powerful questions, and answer a series of previously prepared questions one by one?

- ◉ Perhaps you write down a series of powerful open questions — and pick one per day?

- ◉ Perhaps you take a copy of the eight keys and put it on your fridge so that you can play a new key each time you open the fridge door?

No matter what you do, know that action and reflection will slowly merge as you play: you act while you play — and your play on your inner piano will lead to actions in your life. You reflect while you play — and your play on your inner piano provides further nourishment for reflection in your life. Action and reflection are part and parcel of all the keys.

You may be a person who is very active in the outer world and who reflects less in the inner one? Or maybe you are a person who reflects a lot and has less tendency to act in the outer world? You can benefit from consciously aiming to strengthen your least proficient skill, as it leads to a greater repertoire, more room to manoeuvre, and innovation.

No matter what you do, be aware too that no question is ever "the one true question." Actually, one of the fascinating and fun aspects of playing your inner piano is that you have a vast number of options. As you go along, absorb learning from your own questions: Which ones lead to epiphanies? Which ones seem to sit well with you? Which ones don't seem to land well in your internal maps? Which do you already ask yourself, which do you need to hear more in your life, and which have you never before considered the importance of?

Strengthening your "change muscles"

The whole idea of bringing brain knowledge and a musical mind-set together has been to equip you for the journeys of change you need and want.

As you play your inner piano, you will strengthen your "self-regulation"— the deep, internal mechanism that enables you to engage in mindful, intentional, and thoughtful behaviours.[3] Self-regulation has turned out to be the magic ingredient for a successful life. It contains the ability to adjust yourself, not least

Self-regulation is the magic ingredient for a successful life.

by controlling your impulses, delaying gratification, and taking action that is needed. It is a brain-based capacity that also highly influences workplace productivity.

Longitudinal studies have shown that the ability to self-reg-

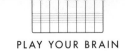

ulate is directly linked to self-esteem, health, academic achievements, quality of friendships and happiness later in life. Sound, self-regulated individuals apply effective mental strategies and brain-based tools. So, you might say there is more to the original formula:

$$\begin{array}{ccccccc} \textit{Brain} & + & \textit{Musical} & \Rightarrow & \textit{Strengthened} & \Rightarrow & \textit{Successful} \\ \textit{knowledge} & & \textit{mindset} & & \textit{self-regulation} & & \textit{change} \end{array}$$

Brain knowledge together with a musical mindset upgrades your ability to adjust relevantly, according to life's circumstances. Thus your self-regulation is strengthened, which in turn strengthens you in all areas of life.

There is musicality in self-regulation too, an ebb and flow — only here you are determining when to hold back and when to move forward, go for gratification or delay it, observe or engage, lead or follow.

As you cultivate this ability, you build up your "change muscles," your ability to focus on your vision and goals, notice differences, shift mental gears, apply constructive beliefs, and be playful, resourceful and resilient, rather than rigid and self-judging.

Thus, in order for this book to become truly useful, you are the one who is now in charge of turning the relevant change you have pondered into successful change in reality.

The ending and the beginning

We have reached our journey's end. But, the ending of this book is also a beginning. You have met yourself and explored your potential; now it is time to create your own unique melodies.

Through this book you have learned to think in a different

way — to apply brain knowledge in a musical way — and that is crucial to creativity and innovation as well as a richer life.

Creativity is adaptability; it's about getting ideas, choosing the most valuable ones, and implementing them in life. You have a good basis for that now, but you have to maintain it. The plastic potential of the brain is only fully harvested when the brain is actively used.

This may be a good place to look out and ahead: How can these tools benefit not only you but also others? In which fields can you make a difference? In what meaningful ways can you involve yourself in our common lives — and contribute to something that is greater than you? Which powerful vision do you want to be a part of — or create? And what aspects of your unique map do you want to contribute and infect others with?

How can these tools benefit not only you but also others?

We have set the tone, and now it is up to you to play your inner piano and make a positive difference in other people's lives through your inner strength and serenity.

Focus your attention on the direction that you want to go. Have a pleasant journey — and enjoy playing!

Glossary

adrenaline — a hormone and a neurotransmitter; increases heart rate, dilates air passages and contributes to the fight-or-flight response of the sympathetic nervous system. (Also known as epinephrine.)

amygdala — part of the limbic system; receives sensory information from all senses; integrates emotional information with the prefrontal cortex; plays a role in expressing emotional behaviour; serves as mediator of fear; responds selectively to faces.

anterior gyrus cinguli — part of the limbic system; rests above the corpus callosum; involved in autonomic functions, as well as emotion (panic), decision-making, empathy and reward anticipation.

cerebral cortex — the outermost surface of the cerebrum; composed of grey matter.

cerebral hemisphere — the cerebrum consists of two cerebral hemispheres: a left and a right.

cerebellum — a hindbrain structure that develops and coordinates complex movement.

cerebrum — the upper portion of the brain.

cognition — the "process of thought"; includes attention, perception, action, emotion, memory, concept-formation, language, music, imagination and problem-solving. Also

considered a social process of education, learning and interaction.

corpus callosum — the largest connection between the two cerebral hemispheres.

cortex — the outer surface of the cerebellum or the cerebrum.

dopamine — an excitatory transmitter produced in several brain regions. The dopamine system is associated with attention, motivation, long-term memory, reward, and drive.

episodic memory — the memory of personal events that can be explicitly stated; together with semantic memory makes up the declarative memory (the counterpart to declarative is implicit memory, also called procedural memory).

frontal lobe — the anterior part of the cerebral hemisphere; contains most of the dopamine-sensitive neurons of the cerebral cortex; separated from the parietal lobe by the motor cortex, which controls planning and execution of voluntary movements. The foremost part is known as the prefrontal cortex.

hippocampus — part of the limbic system; plays an important role in establishing long-term memory and in spatial navigation; generates new neurons from progenitor cells (neurogenesis).

insula — a sensory region for the gut and body. New imaging research has identified further functions — vocalisation and music, time perception, emotional awareness and attention.

limbic system — the system that plays a role in emotional and sexual behaviour as well as motivation and memory; includes the amygdala, the hippocampus and the cingulate cortex.

mirror neurons — a system of neurons that fires both when we act and when we observe the same action performed by another; important in imitative and social learning.

motor cortex — part of the frontal cortex involved in voluntary body movements.

neurohormones — hormones released by neurons that modify the sensitivity of the postsynaptic membrane to neuro-transmitters.

neurotransmitters — transmitters of information from one neuron to another via a chemical compound. The transmitters bind to receptors on the postsynaptic membrane, triggering an all-or-none response. There are more than 100 different neurotransmitters in the brain.

nucleus accumbens — part of the dopaminergic reward system; also plays a role in aggression, fear, laughter and the placebo effect.

orbitofrontal cortex — see *prefrontal cortex*

parietal lobe — the lobe of the cerebral cortex responsible for the analysis of somatosensory stimuli.

phenotype — any observable characteristic or trait of an organism. (By contrast, *genotype* refers to the sum of all inherited information in the organism's genetic code, even if not observable.)

plasticity — malleability; observed in various forms. Neuroplasticity is how brain structures change from experience; synaptic plasticity is a synapse's ability to change its connection; phenotypic plasticity describes the ability to adjust the phenotype in response to the environment.

postsynaptic membrane — the surface of the target cell that receives messages from the presynaptic membrane.

prefrontal cortex — the network linking motor, perceptual and limbic regions; influences and is influenced by almost all brain areas. Can be subdivided into a lateral and a medial (orbitofrontal) part: working memory, expressive language

and gesture, goal-oriented behaviour and planning and selection of action are related to the lateral prefrontal cortex; the medial prefrontal cortex goes in tandem with the lateral, monitoring the emotional content and quality of cognitive control.

serotonin — an excitatory neurotransmitter; found in neurons of the brainstem with widespread projections to the forebrain; regulates sleep and wakefulness.

working memory — a function of the lateral prefrontal cortex that retains information and performs mental operations involving long-term memory. Working memory has a low capacity and can easily be overloaded.

Notes

Introduction

1. DAYAN, P., & L.F. ABBOTT, *Theoretical Neuroscience: Computational and Mathematical Modeling of Neural System* (MIT Press, 2001).

2. See, for example, ROBERTSON, I., *Mind Sculpture: Unleashing Your Brain's Potential* (Bantam Books, 1999).

3. COOPER, R.P., & R.N. ASLIN: "Preference for infant-directed speech in the first month of birth," *Child Development* 61 (5): 1584–95, 1990.

4. GIBSON, C., et al, "Enhanced divergent thinking and creativity in musicians: A behavioral and near-infrared spectroscopy study," *Brain and Cognition* 69 (1): 162–9, 2009.

5. A synapse is the gap between two nerve cells where the transmitter substances conduct impulses.

6. The hippocampus is located in the brain's limbic system and is of great importance to our sense of orientation and memory. It consolidates the semantic memory (our explicit knowledge) and works closely with the lateral part of the frontal lobes.

7. Neurobiologists have recently found a turnover of synapses at the rate of 7 per cent per week in the mouse cortex: *New Scientist*, 5 February 2011.

8. KELSO, J.A.S., *Dynamic Patterns: The Self-organization of Brain and Behavior* (Cambridge: MIT Press, 1995).

9. Neuroplasticity is a rapidly growing scientific field. *Neuro* refers to "neurons," the nerve cells in our brains and nervous system; *plastic* stands for "changeable, easily malleable, modifiable." See DOIDGE, N., *The Brain That Changes Itself* (Penguin Books, 2007).

10. FRANK, L., *Mindfield: How Brain Science is Changing Our World* (Oneworld Publication, 2009). The Fifth Revolution is "the latest in a series of scientific leaps that have overturned the world view and thus created mental and social progress." The five revolutions are (1) Copernicus' realisation in the 16th century that the earth is not the centre of the universe, but simply one of the many planets orbiting the sun; (2) Darwin's theory from the 19th century that all living beings are descendants from the same primitive life-form from which they evolved; (3) Freud's work at the beginning of the 20th century involving the study of the human mind as an objective entity, with all its nooks and crannies and subconscious forces; (4) Watson and Crick's DNA revolution in the middle of the 20th century that uncovered the genome structure, and which made possible the creation and manipulation of life at humanity's discretion; and (5) The discoveries within brain research at the end of the 20th century, which anchored many of the phenomena in the brain's wet cellular substance, and which discovered that the brain can change during one's whole life.

11. See for instance LEHRER, J., *The Decisive Moment* (Canongate, 2009), where he dismisses this notion.

12. Cf. Wellcome Department of Imaging Neuroscience. You can read more at www.wellcome.ac.uk/News/2004/Features/WTX032958.htm, and in SCHWARTZ, J. et al, *The Mind and the Brain: Neuroplasticity and the Power of Mental Force* (Harper Perennial, 2002), p. 250*ff*.

13. DOIDGE, N., *The Brain That Changes Itself* (Penguin, 2007) p. 43.

14. TSUKIURA, T., & R. CABEZA, "Orbitofrontal and hippocampal contribution to memory for face-name associations: The

rewarding power of a smile," *Neuropsychologia* 46 (9): 2310–9, 2008. STRACK, F., et al, "Inhibiting and facilitating conditions of facial expressions: A non-obstructive test of the facial feedback hypothesis," *Journal of Personality and Social Psychology* 54: 768–77, 1988.

1 Thoughts

1. GALLWEY, T., *The Inner Game of Tennis* (Jonathan Cape, 1975), p. 11.

2. SHAPIRO, S., et al, "Cultivating Mindfulness: Effects on Well-Being," *Journal of Clinical Psychology* 64(7): 840–62, 2008; and ROCK, D., *Your Brain at Work* (Harper Business, 2009) p. 91; and HASSED, C., "Mindfulness, well-being, and performance," *NeuroLeadership Journal* 1: 53–60, 2008.

3. TANG, Y.Y., & M.I. POSNER, "The Neuroscience of Mindfulness," *NeuroLeadership Journal* 1 (2008):33–7. TANG, Y.Y., et al, "Short-term meditation training improves attention and self-regulation," *Proceedings of the National Academy of Sciences* 104, no. 43 (2007): 17152–6, 2007.

4. FARB, N.A.S., et al, "Attending to the present: Mindfulness meditation reveals distinct neural modes of self-reference," *Social Cognitive Affective Neuroscience* 2 (2007): 313–22.

5. The slow system of the brain is analytical, explicit, sequential, controlled, and with a low capacity. The fast system of the brain is holistic, implicit, parallel, automatic, and has a large capacity. It is crucial for playing your brain and adopting a musician's mindset that you learn to let these two systems work fluently together. See the Vision key for more on this.

6. ROCK, D., *Your Brain at Work* (Harper Business, 2009), p. 95.

7. SCHOOLER, J.W., et al, "Thoughts beyond words: When language overshadows insight," *Journal of Experimental Psychology* 122, no. 2 (1993): 166–83.

8. BANDURA, A., *Social Foundations of Thought and Action: A Social Cognitive Theory* (Prentice Hall, 1986); and ZIMMERMAN, B.J., "Self-efficacy: An essential motive to learning," *Contemporary Educational Psychology*, 25: 82–91, 2000.

9. GADAMER, H.-G., *Truth and Method* (Crossroad, 2004).

10. ADAMS, M., *Change Your Questions, Change Your Life* (Berrett Koehler, 2004).

11. MARCUS, G., *Kluge: The Haphazard Construction of the Human Mind* (Houghton Mifflin, 2008).

12. From *Zapera*, 2008: www.zapera.com.

13. See COVEY, S., *The Seven Habits of Highly Effective People* (Free Press, 2004).

14. Modern theory on depression asserts that it occurs due to resignation, the feeling that one cannot change one or more unpleasant situations. It is also called "learned helplessness." See SELIGMAN, M., *Learned Optimism* (Vintage, 1990).

15. IYENGAR, S., *The Art of Choosing* (Twelve, 2010).

16. FRANKL, V., *Man's Search for Meaning* (Rider Books, 1959).

17. A subcategory of closed questions are "leading questions." They almost put the answer in the respondent's mouth: "Wouldn't you also like to contribute to the gift?" "Can't you just stop being irritated?"

18. When you both listen to someone's words *and* observe the many clues from their body language, you are carrying out what is referred to as "global listening." See also WHITWORTH, L., et al, *Co-active Coaching* (Davies-Black Publishing, 1998).

2 Values

1. CSÍKSZENTMIHÁLYI, M., *FLOW: The Psychology of Optimal Experience* (Harper Perennial Modern Classics, 2008).

2. Outer and inner characteristics of "flow" experiences include

clear and attainable goals, concentration and focus, loss of self-awareness (integration with actions), distorted concept of time, direct and immediate feedback (allows adaptation of behaviour), an experience of personal control over the situation, living into the activity.

3. ROKEACH, M., *The Nature of Human Value* (Free Press, 1973).

4. Your "map" is what you navigate by in life. It is formed by your experiences and interpretations, your expectations, your defeats and your victories, your fear and your courage, your social communities, your convictions, your theories, and your culture thus far.

5. SPINELLI, E., *Practising Existential Psychotherapy: The Relational World* (SagePublication, 2007).

6. PESSOA, L., "How do emotion and motivation direct executive control?" *Trends in Cognitive Sciences,* 13 (4): 160–66, 2009. WINKIELMAN, P., et al, "Affective Influence on Judgments and Decisions: Movement Towards Core Mechanisms," *Review of General Psychology* 11(2): 179–192, 2007.

7. The cortex is the cerebrum's outermost cell layer, the brain's grey substance which can be divided into four regions: the frontal cortex, the parietal cortex, the occipital cortex, and the temporal cortex.

8. MILGRAM, S., *Obedience to Authority: An Experimental View* (Tavistock, 1974).

9. BAUMAN, Z., *Modernitet og Holocaust* (Hans Reitzels Forlag, 1989).

10. SIMON, H., "Rationality in Economics and Psychology," *Journal of Business,* 59: 4, 1986.

11. READ, P.P., *Alive* (Arrow Books , 2005).

12. Furthermore, it was precisely this suspicion that made Milgram create the experiment. He began his experiments in 1961, shortly after the trial of the Nazi criminal, Eichmann, started in Jerusalem. Could it actually be that Eichmann, and his millions

of accomplices during the Holocaust, just followed orders? And could the rest of us possibly do the same?

13. MILGRAM, S., *Obedience to Authority: An Experimental View* (Tavistock, 1974).

14. "Incongruent" means not in agreement with.

3 Body

1. CARPENTER, S., "Body of Thought," *Scientific American Mind*, January/February 2011.

2. See RIZZOLATTI, G., et al, *Mirrors in the Brain: How Our Minds Share Actions, Emotions and Experience* (Oxford University Press, 2008); and IACOBONI, M., *Mirroring People: The Science of Empathy and How We Connect with Others* (Picador, 2009).

3. One does not get this eye contact and these reactions from an autistic child; there is only the self (*autos* is Greek word for "self"), but it is an isolated self because, in contrast to most of us, it does not reach out to others.

4. For a good description of the experiment and findings, see LEHRER, J., "The Secret of Self-control," in *The New Yorker*, 18 May 2009.

5. Willpower as a concept has been missing in psychological literature for very long. Previously, our mental life was regarded as the interplay between will, emotions, and thought. But today the concept is beginning to gain a foothold. SCHULKIN, J., "Effort and Will: A Cognitive Neuroscience Perspective," *Mind and Matter* 5 (1): 111–26. We look at this further in the Goals chapter.

6. BENNETT-GOLEMAN, T., *Emotional Alchemy* (Harmony, 2001).

7. See the article by BISHOP, S.R., et al, "Mindfulness: A Proposed Operational Definition," available at www.personal.kent. edu/~dfresco/mindfulness/Bishop_et_al.pdf; and see the same source for examples on the documented scientific effects of mindfulness.

8. Pham, T.M., et al, "Effects of neonatal stimulation on later cognitive function and hippocampus nerve growth factor," *Behavioral Brain Research* 86, 113–20, 1997.

9. Zhu, X.O., & Waite, P.M.E., "Cholinergic depletion reduces plasticity of barrel field cortex," *Cerebral Cortex* 8, 63–72, 1998. Myers, W.A., et al, "Role of NMDA receptors in adult primates cortical somatosensory plasticity," *Journal of Comparative Neurology* 418, 373–82, 2000. Cowan, W.M., & E.R. Kandel, "A brief history of synapses and synaptic transmission," in Cowan, W.M., T.C. Sudhof, & C.F. Stevens (ed.), *Synapses* (John Hopkins University Press, Baltimore, 2001), pp. 1–87.

10. Zorawski, M., et al, "Effect of sex and stress on acquisition and consolidation of human fear conditioning," *Learning & Memory* 13: 441–50, 2006.

11. Antonovsky, A., *Unravelling the Mystery of Health* (Jossey-Bass, 1987).

12. Ericsson, K.A., et al, "The Role of Deliberate Practice in the Acquisition of Expert Performance," *Psychological Review* 100, no. 3 (1993): 363–406. Levitin, D., *This is Your Brain on Music: The Science of a Human Obsession* (Dutton, 2006).

4 Perception

1. Reframing, or reappraisal, is the cognitive transformation of emotional experience. See Oshsner, K., et al, "Rethinking Feelings: An fMRI Study of the Cognitive Regulation of Emotion," *Journal of Cognitive Neuroscience* 14:8, pp. 1215–29, 2002.

2. "Preconception" refers to the understanding that we have *before* we encounter something in a specific context. If I have the preconception that young people lack commitment and are dim, it will colour my perception when I find myself face to face with a young person. If I have the preconception that a course I will

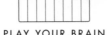

attend is useless and that the teachers are incompetent, it will visibly influence my learning. Therefore, it is important that you are aware of what preconceptions you have. Then you will be able to adjust them in regards to a situation — and get in touch with the curiosity and interest that are crucial for your ability to approach other people and situations with a suitable degree of openness.

3. SENGE, P., in Scharmer, O., *Theory U* (Society for Organizational Learning, 2007), p. xiv.

4. The example is from PREHN, A., "The Brain — A key to Understanding Why Coaching Works," in PREHN, A., et al, *Coaching i Perspektiv* (Hans Reitzels Forlag, 2008). The article can be found at www.where2next.dk/files/13565/1298196168/thebrain-akeytounderstandingwhycoachingworks.pdf.

5. KROSS, E., & O. AYDUK: "Facilitating adaptive emotional analysis: distinguishing distanced-analysis of depressive experiences from immersed-analysis and distraction," *Personality and Social Psychology Bulletin* 34(7), 924–38, 2008.

6. To be "associated" means experiencing a situation via your full emotional spectrum, in your whole body, and looking at it through your own eyes. To be "dissociated" means experiencing a situation from the outside, as if you were seeing it (and yourself) on a movie screen.

7. Rumination means chewing on something at length, going over it again and again. Rumination is one of the known key factors of depression. On top of this it impairs thinking and problem-solving. NOLEN-HOEKSEMA, S., et al, "Rethinking rumination," *Perspectives on Psychological Science* 3, 400–424, 2008.

8. ROBERTSON, I., *Mind Sculpture: Unleashing Your Brain's Potential* (Bantam Books, 1999).

9. HEBB, D., *The Organization of Behavior: A Neuropsychological Theory* (Wiley, 1949).

10. OCHSNER, K., et al, "Rethinking Feelings: An fMRI Study of the Cognitive Regulation of Emotion," *Journal of Cognitive Neuroscience*, vol. 14, no. 8.

11. MAYER, J.D., P. SALOVEY, & D. CARUSO, "Models of emotional intelligence," in STERNBERG, R. (ed.), *Handbook of Intelligence* (Cambridge University Press, 2000).

12. Positive psychology is the scientific study of happiness, well-being, and optimal conditions, functions, and processes. The mission of positive psychology is "to develop sound theories of optimal functioning and to find empirically supported ways to improve the lives of ordinary and extraordinary people." KAUFFMAN, C., "Positive Psychology: The Science at the Heart of Coaching," in STOBER, D., & A. GRANT, *Evidence Based Coaching* (John Wiley & Sons, 2006).

13. QUOIDBACH, J., & E.W. DUNN, "Personality Neglect: The Unforeseen Impact of Personal Dispositions on Emotional Life," *Psychological Science*, Dec 2010, vol. 21. no. 12, 1783–6.

14. The example comes from KLEIN, S., *Die Glücksformel* (Rowolhlt Verlag GmbH, 2002). See also www.gluecksformel.de.

15. Cognitive (behavioural) therapy was developed by Ellis and Beck. The cognitive point of departure is that our emotions and behaviour are largely determined by how we structure our world (using thinking, assumptions, and assessments). Examples of bridge-building between cognitive therapy and coaching can be found in AUERBACH, J., "Cognitive Coaching," in STOBER, D., & A. GRANT, *Evidence Based Coaching* (John Wiley & Sons, 2006).

16. FARB, N., *Mindfulness Meditation Reveals Distinct Neural Modes of Self-reference* (University of Toronto, 2007).

17. One of the relevant factors is mindset. Do you have a "fixed mindset" or a "growth mindset"? See DWECK, C.S., *Mindset: The New Psychology of Success* (Ballantine Books, 2006).

18. KOCH, C., "The New Science of Change," 9 October 2006, www.cio.com.au.

19. MARCUS, G., *Kluge: The Haphazard Construction of the Human Mind* (Houghton Mifflin, 2008).

20. SELIGMAN, M., *Authentic Happiness* (Free Press, 2004).

21. Ibid., and SELIGMAN, M., *Learned Optimism: How to Change Your Mind and Your Life* (Vintage, 2006). Both describe how optimism can be strengthened.

22. BROWN, R.E., & P.M. MILNER, "The Legacy of Donald O. Hebb: More Than the Hebb Synapse," *Nature* 4(12): 1013–9, 2003.

23. *Content reflection* is the examination of the content of a problem; *process reflection* is when you check on the problem-solving strategies; and *premise reflection* is when you question the problem itself. From COX, E., "An Adult Learning Approach to Coaching," in STOBER, D., & A. GRANT, *Evidence Based Coaching* (John Wiley & Sons, 2006).

24. SCHOOLER, J., *Getting to "A-ha,"* The NeuroLeadership Summit 2010, Boston (www.neuroleadership.org/summits/2010_Summit.shtml).

25. ROSENTHAL, R., & L. JACOBSON, *Pygmalion in the Classroom* (Irvington, 1992).

5 Vision

1. SARASVATHY, S., *What Makes Entrepreneurs Entrepreneurial* (2001). www.effectuation.org/ftp/effectua.pdf.

2. The frontal lobes (also called the frontal cortex) can be split into three parts: a medial part, which faces the brain's centre; a lateral part, which faces the ear; and the frontal pole, which faces the forehead. The lateral part is particularly good at working in a structured way, while it is the medial part that can change strategy. The frontal pole is responsible for the memory for the future (see below).

3. ADDIS, D.R., et al, "Remembering the past and imagining the future: Common and distinct neural substrates during event construction and elaboration," *Neuropsychologia* 45: 1363–77, 2007.

4. Memory for the future is the proactive function which can calculate the consequences of one's behaviour, and which is connected to the frontal lobes' frontal pole.

5. KELSO, J.A.S., & D.A. ENGSTRØM, *The Complementary Nature* (Bradford Books, MIT Press, 2006).

6. DIJKSTERHUIS, A., W.B. MAARTEN, L.F. NORDGREN, & R.B. VAN BAAREN, "Making the right choice: The deliberation-without-attention effect," *Science* 311: 1005–7, 2006.

7. LEHRER, J., *The Decisive Moment* (Canongate, 2009).

8. Cognitive psychological processes deal with sensing, emotions, perception, learning, thinking, language, and creativity.

9. Episodic memory is a self-biographical memory, which contains memories of personal experiences (in contrast to semantic memory, which contains memories of factual knowledge).

10. ROCK, D., *Quiet Leadership* (Collins, 2006).

11. ROBERTSON, I., *Mind Sculpture* (Bantam Books, 1999).

12. DES COTEAUX, J.G., & H. LECRERE, "Learning surgical technical skill," *Canadian Journal of Surgery* 38: 33–8, 1995.

13. YUE, G., & K.J. COLE, "Strength increases from the motor program – comparison of training with maximal voluntary and imagined muscle contractions," *Journal of Neurophysiology* 67: 1114–23, 1992.

14. NATARAJA, S., *The Blissful Brain: Neuroscience and Proof of the Power of Meditation* (Gaia Thinking, 2008).

15. BACKLEY, S., et al, *The Winning Mind: A Guide to Achieving Success and Overcoming Failure* (Aurum Press, 1996).

16. SCHOOLER, J., *Getting to "A-ha,"* The NeuroLeadership Summit 2010, Boston.

17. Positive psychology is the scientific study of happiness, well-being, and optimal conditions, functions, and processes.

18. KAUFFMANN, C., "Positive Psychology: The Science at the Heart of Coaching," in STOBER, D., & A. GRANT, *Evidence Based Coaching* (John Wiley & Sons, 2006), p. 220.

6 Goals

1. WHITMORE, J., *Coaching for Performance* (Nicholas Brealey Publishing, 2002).

2. Ibid.

3. CARROLL, L., *Alice in Wonderland* (Simon & Brown, 2010).

4. GRANT, A., "Integrative and Cross Theory Approaches," in STOBER, D., & A. GRANT, *Evidence Based Coaching* (John Wiley & Sons, 2006), p. 161.

5. Ibid.

6. GOLEMAN, D., *Social Intelligence: The New Science of Human Relationships* (Bantam, 2007).

7. GOLLWITZER, P., & J. BARGH, *The Psychology of Action* (Guilford Press, 1996).

8. GAZZANIGA, M.S., et al, *Cognitive Neuroscience: The Biology of the Mind* (W.W. Norton & Company, 2009).

9. "Towards" goals are the same as "approach" goals. "Away from" goals are the same as "avoidance" goals.

10. AMABILE, T., *Creativity in Context: Update to the Social Psychology of Creativity* (Westview Press, 1996).

11. From the limbic system down towards the brainstem's motor pathways, we find a thick bundle of nerve fibres (the medial forebrain bundle, MFB). Here, a secret is buried about how a feeling of well-being and joy can motivate action. MFB is a kind of reward centre. When physiologists study the area, they can

show that the nerve pathway is stimulated by rewards, e.g., when something succeeds and you receive a pat on the shoulder (from yourself or from others). If one needs something, if one is hungry or thirsty, it also increases the activity in the MFB until the need has been satisfied. The reward centre thus motivates action, whether one gets something one values, or one lacks something important. KLEIN, S.B., & B.M. THORNE, *Biological Psychology* (Worth Publisher, 2007).

12. See www.cio.com.au/index.php/id;1653344675;pp;3.

13. MAURER, R., *One Small Step Can Change Your Life: The Kaizen Way* (Workman Publishing Company, 2004).

14. DAVACHI, L., "Learning that lasts through AGES: Maximising the effectiveness of learning initiatives," *NeuroLeadership Journal* 3, 53–63, 2010.

15. See also PETERSON, D., "People Are Complex and the World is Messy: A Behavior-Based Approach to Executive Coaching," in STOBER, D., & A. GRANT, *Evidence Based Coaching* (John Wiley & Sons, 2006).

16. DARLEY, J.M., & C.D. BATSON, "From Jerusalem to Jericho: A Study of Situational and Dispositional Variables in Helping Behavior," *Journal of Personality and Social Psychology* 27 (1973): 100–8.

17. Among other things, the researchers concluded that having the image of the kind-hearted Samaritan at the back of one's mind did not increase the likelihood of helping a person in need. On the other hand, the probability of helping decreased if one was short of time.

7 Emotions

1. GOLEMAN, D., *Social Intelligence: The New Science of Human Relationships* (Bantam, 2007). Goleman offers a series of examples in relation to this: (1) Three or more conditions of intense stress

within a year (e.g., financial difficulties, lay-offs, divorce) triple the risk of death with socially isolated middle-aged men, but these circumstances have absolutely no influence on the mortality of men who have many social relations. (2) The members of 70 work groups, from different lines of business, who held common meetings, ended up sharing similar moods, both positive and negative, within two hours. (3) In cardiac departments where the general mood among nurses was "depressed," the death count was four times higher than at other hospitals.

2. Not least of all in GOLEMAN, D., *Emotional Intelligence: Why It Can Matter More Than IQ* (Bantam, 2006); GOLEMAN, D., *Social Intelligence: The New Science of Human Relationships* (Bantam, 2007). Daniel Goleman generated quite a stir with his concept of "Emotional Intelligence" when he published his book by the same name in 1995. He got the term from Professor Peter Salovey.

3. GOLEMAN, D., et al, *Primal Leadership: Learning to Lead with Emotional Intelligence* (Harvard Business Press, 2004).

4. Resonance comes from *resonare* (Latin); it is an amplification of a sound reflected back from a surface.

5. BENNETT-GOLEMAN, T., *Emotional Alchemy* (Harmony Books, 2001). Mindfulness is a trained mental state characterised by a calm awareness that the perception of one's body's functions, thoughts, and emotions takes place in one's mind. It is the ability to see things exactly as they are, moment by moment. Instead of letting oneself be carried away (or becoming preoccupied by a thought or an emotion), one calmly observes these thoughts and emotions while they come and go. In full attention, you drawn upon an ability to be dissociated, and unattached in relation to your own thoughts and emotions. Mindfulness techniques are frequently used within Western psychology to relieve various mental and physical conditions. The focus is on the "pure" experience in the present as well as on a "curious, open, and accepting" approach to this experience; see BISHOP,

S.R., et al, "Mindfulness: A Proposed Operational Definition," available at www.personal.kent.edu/~dfresco/mindfulness/Bishop_et_al.pdf.

6. WISEMAN, R., *59 Seconds: Think A Little, Change A Lot* (Macmillan, 2009).

7. The Duchenne smile is named after its discoverer, Guillaume Duchenne. See also SELIGMAN, M., *Authentic Happiness* (Free Press, 2004).

8. SELIGMAN, M., *Authentic Happiness* (Free Press, 2004).

9. MULLEN, B., et al, "Newscasters' Facial Expressions and Voting Behavior of Viewers: Can a Smile Elect a President?" *Journal of Personality and Social Behavior*, 51(2): 291–5, 1986.

10. GARY, L.W., & R.E. PETTY, "The Effects of Overt Head Movements on Persuasion," *Basic and Applied Social Psychology* 1(3): 219–30, 1980.

11. ARONOFF, J., et al, "Which are the stimuli in facial display of anger and happiness? Configurational bases of emotion recognition," *Journal of Personality and Social Psychology* 62: 1050–66, 1992.

12. DAVIS, J.I., et al, "The effects of Botox injections on emotional experience," *Emotion* 10(3), June 2010, pp. 433–40.

13. ZAJONC, R.B., "Brain temperature and subjective emotional experience," in LEWIS, M., & J.M. HAVILAND (eds.), *Handbook of Emotions* (New York, Guildford, 1993), pp. 209–20.

14. The limbic system is also called the "emotional brain," and is the part of the brain which is located between the brainstem and the cerebrum. It is a complex, ring-shaped structure, which includes the hypothalamus, the amygdala, the hippocampus.

15. CONDON, W.S., "Cultural Microrhythms," in DAVIS, M. (ed.), *Interaction Rhythms: Periodicity in Communicative Behavior* (New York, 1982), pp. 53–76.

16. FILSINGER, E.E., & S.J. THOMA, "Behavioral Antecedents of Relationship Stability and Adjustment: A Five-Year Longitudinal Study," *Journal of Marriage and the Family*, 1988, pp. 785–95; and GOTTMAN, J.M., *What Predicts Divorce?* (Laurence Erlbaum Associates, 1994).

17. See COX, E., "An Adult Learning Approach to Coaching," in STOBER, D., & A. GRANT, *Evidence Based Coaching* (John Wiley & Sons, 2006).

18. GOLEMAN, D., *Social Intelligence: The New Science of Human Relationships* (Bantam, 2007).

19. The amygdala detects signs of fear in a person's face in a glimpse of 33 milliseconds (with some people it is just 17 milliseconds). Sensory perception evades consciousness; we are infected long before any conscious awareness. It was a huge advantage when we lived in groups in the woods, and it is still useful for sensing the "temperature" of a given situation; we use each other to understand and to gain meaning regarding a situation.

20. LEDOUX, J., *The Emotional Brain* (Simon & Schuster, 1998).

21. BENNETT-GOLEMAN, T., *Emotional Alchemy* (Harmony, 2001).

22. Ibid.

23. ROCK, D., "Managing with the Brain in Mind," *Strategy+Business*, 27 August 2009, www.strategy-business.com/article/09306?g ko=5df7f&cid=enews20091013, introduces the SCARF model (status, certainty, autonomy, relatedness and fairness).

24. ROBERTSON, I., *Mind Sculpture: Unleashing Your Brain's Potential* (Bantam Books, 1999).

25. ROOZENDAAL, B., et al, "Stress, memory and the amygdala," *Nature Review Neuroscience* 10: 423–33, 2009.

26. LUDERS, E., et al, *The underlying anatomical correlates of long-term meditation: Larger hippocampal and frontal volumes of gray matter*, www.sciencedirect.com, 14 January 2009.

27. HUANG, E.J., & L.F. REICHARDT, "Neurotrophins: Roles in neuronal development and function," *Annual Review of Neuroscience* 24: 677–736, 2001. BDNF supports the survival of certain existing neurons, and boosts the growth and differentiation of new neurons and synapses. It is active in the hippocampus and other areas vital to learning and higher thinking. BDNF itself is important for the formation of long-term memory.

28. MORGENSTERN, S., *Composers on Music: An Anthology of Composers' Writings from Palestrina to Copland* (Pantheon, 1975).

8 Successes

1. TAKAHASHI, H., et al, "When Your Gain Is My Pain and Your Pain Is My Gain: Neural Correlates of Envy and Schadenfreude," *Science*, 13 February 2009, vol. 323, no. 5916, pp. 937–9; and LIEBERMAN, M., & N. EISENBERGER, "Pains and Pleasures of Social Life," *Science*, 13 February 2009, pp. 890–1.

2. KANDEL, E., et al, "Cognitive Neuroscience and the Study of Memory," *Neuron*, vol. 20, 445–68, Mar 1998; and DUGGAN, W., "How Aha! really happens," *Strategy+Business* 61, 23 Nov 2010.

3. Brain waves are divided into the following groups:

    25–42+ Hz: Gamma (Beta2): the mental accelerator; high activity in the brain; deep concentration and focus; peak performances; insights

    16–24 Hz: Beta (Beta1): concentration, thinking, perception, problem solving, and active attention directed towards the outer world

    12–15 Hz: SMR: intimacy, relaxation, and integration of impulses

    8–12 Hz: Alfa: inward-focused attention, relaxation, balance, reflection

    4–7 Hz: Theta: subconscious activity associated with emotions, drowsiness, dreams

    0.5–4 Hz: Delta: basic survival functions originating deep in the brain; deep sleep

4. A neurotransmitter is a chemical substance, such as serotonin and dopamine, which is involved in the transfer of impulses from one nerve cell to another. There are some 60 neurotransmitters, of which some are conducive and some are inhibiting.

5. KOUNIOS, J., et al, "The Prepared Mind: Neural Activity Prior to Problem Presentation Predicts Subsequent Solution by Sudden Insight," *Psychological Science*, 17(10): 882–90, 2006.

6. DUGGAN, W., "How Aha! really happens," *Strategy+Business* 61, 23 November 2010.

7. ROCK, D., *Quiet Leadership* (Collins, 2006).

8. DWECK, C.S., *Self-Theories: Their Role in Motivation, Personality, and Development* (Psychology Press, Taylor & Francis Group, 2000).

9. DWECK, C.S., *Mindset: The New Psychology of Success* (Ballantine Books, 2006). However, it is important to add that we all have both forms of mindset, and that the fixed mindset can work as an effective autopilot. It ensures that we can perform a task with great certainty, as long as the action is in harmony with the situation.

10. ERICSSON, K.A., et al, *The Cambridge Handbook of Expertise and Expert Performance* (Cambridge University Press, 2006).

11. It is possible to have one type of mindset in a certain area, and another in a different area.

12. LEHRER, J., *The Decisive Moment* (Canongate, 2009).

13. SELIGMAN, M., *Learned Optimism* (Vintage, 2006).

9 All together now!

1. Neuroscientist Charles S. Sherrington wrote in his 1942 book, *Man On His Nature*: "It is as if the Milky Way entered upon some cosmic dance. Swiftly the head mass becomes an enchanted loom where millions of flashing shuttles weave a dissolving pattern,

always a meaningful pattern though never an abiding one; a shifting harmony of subpatterns."

2. To calibrate means to align two instruments to each other. In coaching, calibration is used to understand what other people mean to say with the words they choose to use. When one calibrates, one aims to understand the subjective meaning behind words or sentences.

3. BUTLER, D.L., & P.H. WINNE: "Feedback and self-regulated learning: A theoretical synthesis," *Review of Educational Research* 65, 245–81, 1995; and BODROVA, E., & D.J. LEONG, "Developing Self-regulation in Kindergarten" (2008), www.naeyc.org/files/ yc/file/200803/BTJ_Primary_Interest.pdf.

Acknowledgments

Anette Prehn would like to thank:

Nishiki Sano, Joern Pedersen, Line Fredens, and Rune Thomassen, for loving music and working through your hearts; Allan Madsen, for showing me that one does not understand the beginning until one knows the end; Jesper Marcussen, Kim Oestroem & co., for nurturing that unique editorial environment back then; and Jens Eiken, my husband, for your love, flexibility, and gorgeous gourmet cooking while I played with this book.

Dedicated to baby Alicia, who was with *Play Your Brain* and me every step of the way — as I will be with you.

Both authors would like to thank:

Martin Liu, our publisher, for the respect and faith you have shown this book, and your spot-on feedback;

Justin Lau, our editor, for your great support and the most inspiring ping-pong;

Philip Johnson, from the Danish Embassy in London, for loving *Play Your Brain* from the beginning — it would not be here without you!

ANETTE PREHN is an award-winning trainer, leadership consultant, thinker, public speaker, sociologist (M.A.), and professional certified coach (International Coach Federation). Specialising in how to apply the insights of neuroscience to human interaction, result-optimisation and change, Anette has worked with executives, managers, and teams in numerous organisations, and is also a guest lecturer at Copenhagen Business School. She has published two books in Danish. In 2009, Anette was awarded the title "Trainer of the Year (Leadership/Coaching)" by Confex.
⇨ WWW.ANETTEPREHN.COM

KJELD FREDENS is a medical doctor, independent brain researcher, thinker, innovator and highly sought-after public speaker. He has worked in the field of neurobiology for more than 35 years, and has been associate professor of neurobiology (brain research) at the University of Aarhus, director of research and development at a rehabilitation centre, principal of a teacher-training college, and editor of the Danish magazine, *Cognition & Education*. He is an adviser of competence and recipient of the FTF Culture Prize. His special interests are the actions and mental processes that lead to learning, innovation and co-operation. Kjeld has written eight books.

⇨ WWW.PLAYYOURBRAIN.COM